0852 429460 1 002

D0358170

BOOKS SHOULD BE RETURNED ON OR BEFO
SHOWN BELOW. BOOKS NOT ALREADY REC
READERS MAY BE RENEWED BY PERSONA
WRITING, OR BY TELEPHONE TO RENEW GIVE TI
NUMBER ON TH

SURPLUS
2-WAY RADIO
CONVERSION
HANDBOOK

SURPLUS
2-WAY RADIO
CONVERSION
HANDBOOK

CHRIS·LOREK

ARGUS BOOKS

Argus Books
Argus House
Boundary Way
Hemel Hempstead
Hertfordshire
England

First published by Argus Books 1989

© Chris Lorek 1989

All rights reserved. No part of this publication may be
reproduced in any form, by print, photography, microfilm
or any other means without written permission from
the publisher.

ISBN 0 85242 946 0

LEABHARLANNA ATHA CLIATH
WALKINSTOWN LIBRARY
ACC. NO.   0852 429460
COPY NO.   WA 1002
INV NO/90 1821
PRICE IR£   11.70
CLASS 621·38 4165

Phototypesetting by GCS, Leighton Buzzard, Bedfordshire.
Printed and bound in Great Britain by Richard Clay Ltd, Bungay, Suffolk.

CONTENTS

ACKNOWLEDGEMENTS

I am indebted to the Publications and Publicity Departments of Philips Telecom, for their help and assistance in preparation of material for this book, and for their kind permission in allowing the reproduction of diagrams and photographs.

Thanks also go to the editor of 'Ham Radio Today' magazine for permission to reproduce extracts and diagrams from previously published articles.

Last, but not least, my thanks to my wife Sheila, and to my young family of Steven, David, and Carolyn, for their patience in putting up with my long days and nights sat at the word processor.

INTRODUCTION

This book was not planned, nor was it even dreamed about, when I first wrote a conversion article in a local repeater group newsletter I produced, giving details on tuning and modifying Pye 'Pocketphone 70' portable transceivers on to the 70 cm amateur band from lessons learnt, often the hard way, from personal experiences.

In the past, the surplus equipment conversion field was often a job for the 'technical experts' who had access to professional test equipment, such as radio frequency signal generators and the like, coupled with the essential manufacturer's service manual (or more often, a third or fourth generation photocopy handed along from one amateur to the other). If you knew of such a person, you were in luck, and if you could accompany them to a rally where the surplus equipment was normally sold in great profusion you'd often end up with a bargain rig suitable for amateur radio use. Very often, some pieces of surplus equipment may look identical from the outer case if they are from the manufacturer's same 'series' but internally they could be *totally* different, sometimes proving unsuitable for use on the amateur bands. The layman would sometimes purchase a set because it 'looked like' the set his friend had successfully converted, and then be severely disappointed.

With this in mind, the Pocketphone 70 article first gave details of which sets to look for, for example how to identify a UHF FM set from a VHF AM set by examination of the rear label. This was followed by simple tuning instructions using the absolute minimum of test equipment, and certainly nothing that wouldn't already be found in the average radio amateur's 'shack', together with a simple toneburst circuit that may be internally fitted to the set. Within a few weeks literally hundreds of photocopies of this article were known to be 'doing the rounds' – the floodtide gates had certainly opened!

The national amateur radio magazines were not slow in realizing this current information gap, and a highly successful conversion series covering several equipments followed in 'Ham Radio Today' magazine. From the amount of feedback that resulted from this, I had my arm twisted on numerous occasions to produce this book! So here we are, I hope it proves useful and shows how, with simple or even no test gear, you can get a professional quality transceiver operational on the amateur bands for very little cost.

This book covers the majority of Pye surplus equipment available. Old valve-technology sets, such as the Cambridge and Vanguard equipments, are not covered, neither are current up-to-date sets which normally fetch high prices on the professional market. Other makes of equipment are occasionally found on the market but Pye sets vastly predominate in this field, hence their coverage in this book.

1 TWO-WAY RADIO—AN INTRODUCTION

Two-way radio takes many forms. The type this book is concerned about is Private Mobile Radio, commonly referred to as PMR. On the 13th August 1947, the Camtax taxi company in Cambridge fitted the first PMR system to be used in the UK, consisting of vehicle-mounted radio equipment operating on VHF supplied by Pye. From that day on, businesses throughout the country have realized the advantages that closer communication can bring, and many would be severely hampered, if they could exist at all, without the use of PMR.

Take the case of a local express pickup and delivery service, for instance, where speed of service is very important. The driver picks up a package from one side of the city for delivery several miles

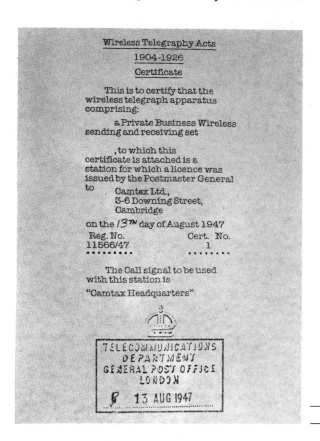

The first ever UK PMR licence issued.

away, while on his way to the delivery point he receives a message informing him of his next pickup point and so on. If he did not use two-way radio he'd need to constantly be returning to base to receive further instructions or forever be trying to find a working phone box, both of which waste precious time and fuel. Every day, more and more people are realizing the advantages of PMR to make the best available use of their resource. Even I saw the advantage of instant communication several years ago – I now use a wide coverage Common-Base-Station PMR system to communicate with my wife/secretary! However the popular benefits of PMR do have an adverse side-effect and, as we shall see, this is sometimes bad news for PMR users but often very good news for radio amateurs!

Frequency Congestion

At the time of writing (1988), the usage of two-way radio is at such a level that in many areas severe frequency congestion is evident. As time goes by, more and more people become operational using PMR and, as the radio frequency spectrum is not a limitless band, it cannot be 'stretched'. In the past, as radio design technology improved, higher and higher frequencies could be pressed into service. In the early days, the lower frequency VHF bands were used, followed by higher VHF frequencies, then UHF in the 460 MHz range. This has the effect of releasing more channels, but eventually they do get filled up and other means of spectrum conservation must be used.

Initially, channels were separated by a 50 kHz frequency spacing. This was because of stability limitations of crystals employed at the time; as technology improved, with components that did not 'drift' as much in frequency, the channel spacing was halved to 25 kHz hence effectively doubling the number of available channels. As time went on, more and more people came on the air, and the channel spacing once again was halved to 12.5 kHz, initially on VHF and then UHF. Also, as more and more equipment became used, the possibility of interference to other services became worrying. Hence, tighter and tighter specifications were brought into force, to ensure lower levels of harmonic radiation from the transmitter and better adjacent channel rejection in the receiver, for instance, leading to better and better equipment being required to 'keep up with the times'.

This state of affairs is nothing new; the congestion has been increasing all the time and anyone who has tried to get an 'exclusive' channel in a large city will tell you horror stories of the time delay involved before getting a licence. Frequencies released to PMR from the early TV Band III are now being employed using trunked dynamic-channel allocation methods in an effort to improve the situation.

Good News for Amateurs

Why am I saying all this and why is this good news for radio amateurs? Well, as the commercial lads need to be constantly upgrading their equipment to maintain good communication, what happens to all the old gear? It gets sold as 'Electronic Scrap' at ridiculously low prices! The knowledgeable radio amateur then buys the equipment, plugs in a couple of crystals, spends an hour or so aligning the set and, hey presto, he has an economic set that allows him to chat away to his heart's content on the amateur band of his choice!

Simple Controls

As PMR equipments need to be used by a wide range of operators, from delivery van drivers to police officers, the use of the equipment should detract as little as possible from the actual job in hand, i.e. that of driving, supervising, controlling traffic or whatever. As a result, PMR equipment is essentially simple to operate, with many sets having little if anything more than a volume control, PTT and on/off switch, sometimes but not always with a squelch and channel switch thrown in for good measure.

Safe Driving

In the UK, much has been said about the dangers of using complicated equipment while driving, especially dialling and conversing on car telephones with their sophisticated displays and functions. It has been shown in the UK press that *controlling* an average synthesised all-singing, all-dancing amateur transceiver i.e. changing channel by viewing the frequency on an LCD, changing the step size, selecting repeater shift etc, is *considerably* more hazardous than using a fist mic to speak into. An independent American study (Bell) confirms this.

One solution of course is to control the set using a minimum of knobs and buttons, exactly what we have in PMR equipment. By using crystalled channels and a click-step channel switch with a defined 'start' position, such as Channel 1, we can indeed operate by touch alone with no need to take our eyes off the road. There is no need to remember to select repeater shift when going to a repeater frequency as this is automatically provided for us with our crystal selection.

Rugged Construction

Equipments such as handportables often have to be used in exposed or hazardous environments, such as out in the pouring rain or on oil rigs. They also need to carry on working if they are accidentally dropped as somebody's life may indeed depend on it.

Because of this, you'll often find ex-PMR portable equipment far, far better for uses such as Raynet on dedicated channels than the average amateur 'black box' that needs a training course in its use as well as cracking open the second it gets a knock.

Repeaters

The majority of amateur repeaters in use in the UK at present use ex-PMR base station equipment (and, indeed, one or two groups have purchased new PMR equipment especially for this). There is one simple reason for this, and that is their good performance. Many repeaters are placed into operation on remote hill-top sites, these often being shared with many other radio users. Because of this, all radio equipments used must be of impeccable technical performance, they must receive the wanted signal only whilst rejecting other neighbouring transmitter signals to a considerable degree, and they must be very 'clean' in their transmitted spectrum, so as not to degrade the performance of neighbouring receivers through the generation of wide-band noise and the like. Last, but not least, they must be very reliable as the equipment runs 24 hours a day, which puts stringent demands on its reliability. It would be very annoying if the repeater were constantly to break down, and hence require frequent trips to a wind-swept hill-top in the middle of nowhere by a pressed repeater group technical volunteer.

Amateur Advantages

From this we can see that, in many respects, surplus PMR equipment has much to offer and, in several cases, is at an advantage to normal purpose-designed amateur equipment built to an economic cost. In these cases it is certainly *not* a poor man's replacement to the latest Japanese wonder-box. Having said this, though, it would be wrong to say that it would be ideal for the person who requires a reasonable number of channels on a band such as 2 m or 70 cm. If you need all the repeater and commonly used simplex channels, for instance, the cost of the crystals alone could very easily approach the price of a dedicated, synthesised amateur transceiver.

However, for use on one or two dedicated channels, for packet radio, Raynet, or bands such as 4 m, it is ideal. It is for these uses that I have written this book.

2 TYPES OF EQUIPMENT

FREQUENCY BANDS

The majority of sets found on the surplus PMR market are, naturally, designed to operate on PMR frequencies which are normally different to the frequency allocations of our amateur bands. In many cases, the built-in 'overlap' by the equipment manufacturer renders a set which, although designed to operate only from 146 MHz or 148 MHz upwards, is quite capable of performing on 145 MHz without degradation. In some cases, an amateur band occurs right in the middle of the allowable operating range; for example an 'E' band equipment covering 68–88 MHz will operate on the 70 MHz amateur band.

The equipment detailed in this book is generally designed to operate on one or more of the following commercial bands.

Band Designation	Freq. Range (MHz)	Nearest Amateur Band
G	32.5–40	10 m (28–29.7 MHz)
H	40–50	6 m (50–52 MHz)
E	68–88	4 m (70–70.5 MHz)
B	132–156	2 m (144–146 MHz)
A	148–174	2 m (144–146 MHz)
T	405–440	70 cm (430–440 MHz)
U	440–470	70 cm (430–440 MHz)

Note that these bands are 'approximate' frequency ranges, in practice, they are often suffixed with a number to indicate frequency variations. For instance, 'A' band is sometimes extended down to 146 MHz for one range of equipment but remains at a lower limit of 148 MHz for another. In the following chapters covering equipment modifications, each equipment type with its associated original manufactured ranges will be detailed.

4 m 4 m offers the advantages of a 'quiet' band but with extended communication range compared to 2 m or 70 cm. The main reason for it being 'quiet' is not for any technical reasons, but because it is a band common only to the UK and Gibraltar and, as a result, there are very few (if any at all) commercial amateur transceivers now made for this band. The only equipments available to my knowledge at the time of writing are 'add-ons' such as transverters, transmitter power amplifiers, and receiver pre-amplifiers. 4 m is hence the band of the 'dedicated few', and is ideal for a relatively private natter net or for dedicated group communication uses such as Raynet.

'E' band sets are ideal for 4 m. This is a very common band in UK PMR usage and there is an abundance of surplus equipment here. There is, however, one exception in equipment operating over this frequency band, and that is the Pocketphone 70 range where the band is split into two sections, E1 and E2. An E2 band set as a result may often require a few component modifications to allow correct operation. These are detailed in the following chapter on portable equipment, but take care when hunting for your 4 m FM portable on the rally stand and take a look at the rear frequency label.

Band Usage

You will find that some areas use AM and FM but others exclusively FM on the amateur 4 m band so, when searching for gear, don't turn your nose up at an AM transceiver, it may be that all your fellow club members merrily chat away to each other using this mode on 70.260 MHz. With this in mind, in the following chapters I will be giving details covering some of the commonly available 4 m AM mobile transceivers such as Westminsters, Motafones and Olympics, as well as several FM portables, mobiles, and base stations for the band.

You'll find the majority of AM activity occurs on 70.260 MHz, with the occasional FM QSO taking place here also. This has been a dedicated mobile calling and general natter channel for many years now. FM activity invariably takes place on 70.450 MHz, this being used for calling as well as general nattering in quiet areas. Other channels used for QSYing purposes following an initial contact on 70.450 MHz are the adjacent frequencies of 70.425 MHz and 70.475 MHz; if or when activity increases still further we may find the intermediate 12.5 kHz frequencies also being used.

2 m The 2 m band is currently the most active VHF/UHF band in the UK, the majority of Class-B licencees starting their operating days here. 'B' band sets, where the amateur 2 m band lies nicely in the middle, are unfortunately very rare in the UK as these have mainly been manufactured for export 'A' band sets, however, are often capable of tuning to 2 m with no difficulty at all, so this is the type we will be basing the majority of the tuning details on. As with 4 m, there is one exception to this, and that again is the Pocketphone 70 range where the band is split into two sections, A1 and A2. An A2 set may require some component changes to operate correctly on 2 m and these are detailed in the chapter on portable equipment.

Due to the exclusive use of FM rather than AM on 2 m, AM equipment conversions have not been detailed. Please *don't* be tempted to buy a cheap AM set and think it economical to convert it to FM – it isn't. With the abundance of FM equipment, at prices from £1 upwards, it is sheer folly to spend several pounds on components and add-on boards to fit an extra FM discriminator and modulator to your set, often getting a compromise in the resultant performance.

Band Usage

Due to its popularity, you will find you will need a number of channels for simplex communication in many areas, purely to allow you to be able to find a clear channel on which to talk. 145.500 MHz (Channel S20) is used for general calling and, in most of the UK, it is normal practice to immediately clear this by QSYing to one of the simplex communication channels allocated in the bandplan (you will find this in the Appendix). Because of the number of channels often required, it must be said that, for general use as a base station or as a country-wide mobile set, it would often be more economic to purchase a dedicated synthesised amateur transceiver.

As an alternative, if you are simply interested in a 'bolt in the car and leave it' set for local use, you will find that crystalling your set up on your local repeater plus a couple of simplex channels will be perfectly adequate for occasional use or as a low-cost 'starter' for the band. The Appendix gives details of the locations and frequencies of 2 m repeaters in the UK at the time of writing.

Packet Radio

The frequency of 144.650 MHz currently holds the most active packet radio network in the UK, operating on FM. The secondary frequency of 144.675 MHz is often used for one-to-one QSOs between individual amateurs in busy areas. Packet radio may be new to many readers but it is the fastest growing mode of amateur communication. Briefly, it is automatic, error-free computer communication: what you type at your terminal or computer gets arranged into 'packets' of information by a small 'Terminal Node Controller' box acting as an interface between your FM transceiver and your terminal. These 'packets' are transmitted as short bursts, in such a way as to allow many QSOs to take place all using the same frequency.

Throughout day and night, automatic mailbox stations forward messages to and from amateurs across the country, unattended network 'node' stations communicate with each other, constantly finding paths between them to use for the amateurs who 'connect' into them for communication with each other. Remote satellite uplink stations connect to packet store-and-forward message handling stations orbiting the earth.

The result is worldwide, 100% error-free communication, using nothing more than your 2 m FM rig coupled to your TNC and terminal. Amateurs who already have a commercial rig have found it advantageous to leave it connected up and operational on packet radio 24 hrs a day, to receive and store messages from other amateurs in their absence, and to allow others to use their station as an automatic 'digipeater'. These amateurs have similarly found their £500 transceiver permanently 'tied up' on this single frequency! Because of this, a dedicated low-cost FM set such as a re-tuned PMR set is ideal for packet use. Because of the high degree of channel occupancy, a high transmit power is not required, neither is a very sensitive receiver. Many amateurs have found a 'Pye Westminster' or 'Europa' perfect for this, so you now know what to look out for.

70 cm Many years ago no-one except the very rich would dream of buying a stand-alone 70 cm black box as there was just not the activity to justify it. However, 2 m is getting rather crowded and amateurs are seeking new pastures to have a relaxed natter, the 'next band up' of 70 cm being the most likely choice. Due to the shorter wavelength, 70 cm can get around built up areas far better than 2 m, as the majority of communication here is achieved by reflection from buildings, and so on. Due to this better penetration in towns, you'll find that you only need a small aerial on your car or handportable to achieve good signals and hence reliable communication. You will, however, find that over longer distances, such as between towns or cities, 70 cm offers more path loss and hence weaker signals, and here you may be better served by using 2 m or 4 m frequencies.

On UHF PMR equipments, all manufactured sets have been FM, and as a result are eminently suitable for use on 70 cm. 'T' band equipments are fairly scarce, although there have been some released onto the market that have seen use in PMR 'Common Base Station' service with sub-audible tone boards fitted, Europas and Olympics for example. The majority available on the market are on U band, and you will find that in most cases these will tune to 70 cm adequately, but the receiver sections on mobiles such as the Westminster's and Europa's may only operate correctly if you obtain the correct crystals, as detailed in the following chapter on these equipments. Beware of so-called 'ex-stock' crystals for these offered by some crystal dealers.

Band Usage
70 cm FM operation now has become *the* amateur 'community' system in many areas of the country, through the very large number

of 70 cm repeaters around the country, these being officially dedicated to provide 'community' coverage. These are detailed in the Appendix, where you will see these considerably outnumber those operating on 2 m. There is rarely the need to QSY to a simplex frequency as, due to the lower level of activity, most amateurs on the local 'community' repeater know each other and are quite happy to have 'net' type contacts with many stations all joining in. Here, of course, is where an ex-PMR set crystalled up on just the local repeater and possibly one or two simplex frequencies such as SU20 (433.500) and SU22 (433.550) is ideal for local use.

Remote and Dash Mount Sets

For mobile equipment, you will sometimes find two types of mounting are available, these being dash and remote mounted sets. Dash mount is the most common, especially with later sets of small size, and the equipment is generally self-contained with all controls and switches on the facia, and sometimes but not always having a built-in speaker on the front panel. Being self-contained, these are the most popular amongst amateurs but early sets, such as the Westminster series, are a little on the large size for today's compact car interiors, although they are often fine for base station use.

Remote mount sets are designed to be fitted in places such as the boot or under the seats in a vehicle, with a long multi-way 'umbilical' cable linking the main body of the set to a small control box having the usual volume, squelch, and channel change controls, together with the microphone and speaker connections. These are favoured by many commercial users, and may be of advantage to amateurs who wish to have a tidy, neat dashboard with the sets themselves hidden away from view and possible theft. I remember one occurrence many years ago, where a thief entered my car in an attempt to steal the radio equipment. He was foiled by the control boxes in the car linked to my three remote-mount Westminster's (on 4 m, 2 m and 70 cm) which were secured in the boot with padlocks through a small hole drilled into the side of the chassis of each, and he left empty-handed.

Where To Find The Bargains

Several companies in the UK provide a mail order service for surplus equipment, through which you will often be able to get good quality gear at reasonable prices. One or two others have, in the past, run regular auctions of surplus gear, often selling individual types of equipments in lots of 10 or 15 sets at a time, ideal for group or club purchase. A list of dealers is in the Appendix.

However, for the individual amateur, by far the best bargains are to be found at the many radio rallies taking place throughout the year

PF1's by the boxful!

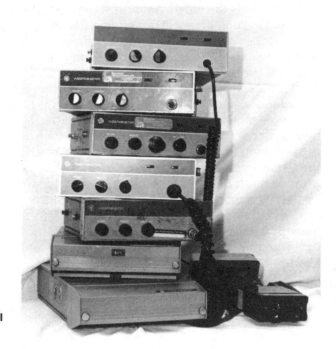

Westminsters of all shapes and sizes.

in all parts of the country. In the past, I have found the best of these for surplus gear to be the Elvaston Castle Rally in Derbyshire, and the Old Warden boot sale in Bedfordshire. Other local rallies and the odd surplus equipment ('junk') sale can often lead to bargains being snapped up if you know what to look for (take this book with you). If you are prepared to do a little haggling, you will sometimes find a cheaper price results, or extras such as a spare battery or leather case for your handportable 'thrown in'.

As an example, at my local rally in Peterborough one year, I purchased a brand new Pye SSB1000T 1 kW (yes!) HF transmitter complete with all the electronics but minus the cabinet, for the sum of £2 (after haggling – the original price asked was £5). At the same rally, Pye Olympics were being sold at two for £1. I cannot really fix a price onto various types of gear, because the law of 'supply and demand' often holds very true. If there are many similar items for sale at an individual rally, and one of the traders wishes to sell all his stock that day, the price of all of these sets will often plummet. As time goes by, also, various types of equipment will be released from a large user such as the Home Office, and the value of such gear will often change drastically overnight. One thing is certain, though: even if the price does change, you will very rarely have been 'ripped off' in the first place unless you have ignored my advice, for example buying an AM set with the hope of converting it to FM, or purchasing the wrong frequency range.

Many types of equipment form part of a *range*, being housed in identical cases but having completely different electronics inside. Don't be misled by your friend pointing to a cased-up set in the Pocketphone 70 range and telling you "That's a 70 cm FM rig" or whatever, simply because it 'looks like' the one he's got. So read through the book carefully, take note of what the metal equipment serial number label on the equipment states (if it has been removed – leave well alone!), and happy rally hunting!

3   ALIGNMENT TECHNIQUES

You will find that the majority, if not all, of two-way radio equipment is capable of operating over a small frequency range, typically a few MHz, forming a sub-section of the much larger frequency range the equipment was designed to operate on. A typical example is that of a mobile operating on 169.0125 MHz to 169.5750 MHz on a few crystalled channels, whereas the set itself was built with the facility of covering any small section of 146–174 MHz.

This is because tuned Inductor/Capacitor circuit stages are used to select the correct crystal oscillator harmonic in the frequency multiplication stages; also in the receiver front end the desired band is allowed to pass with minimum attenuation, but to reject the 'image' frequency that would otherwise occur.

This re-tune facility is of course very useful, because it means that on the vast majority of equipments detailed in this book, by simply making adjustments rather than component modifications, a set that originally operated on 169 MHz for example may be made to operate perfectly on 145 MHz. 'Conversion' in this context then simply means 're-tuning' rather than long evenings spent with a soldering iron and a bag full of components!

In a small number of cases, for instance with the VHF Pocketphone 70 range, the original sets were made to cover only a 'sub-band' and hence may require a few capacitor changes to achieve optimum performance but I will detail these changes if required. Other conversion projects detailed are those of transforming a pager receiver into a top-pocket 2 m monitor, a 68–88 MHz A200 into a high-performance 6 m linear amplifier, and a UHF Westminster into a 70 cm repeater.

Trimming Tools

The equipments detailed commonly have tuning elements made up of adjustable ferrite cores in wound coils and metal or ceramic trimmer capacitors. It is very important to use the correct type of adjusting tools for these, for several reasons. Golden rule number one is that whatever you use, it *must not* be metallic. If you insert a piece of metal into an inductor, when for instance you adjust a ferrite core, you will radically affect the inductance value, so that as soon as you remove the adjuster you will find your circuit has instantly gone 'off tune'.

Trimming tools are useful.

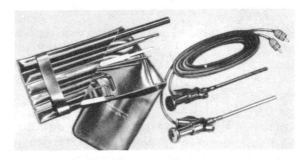

A very important warning is *never*, and I repeat *never* be tempted to use one of the commonly available types of jeweller's screwdrivers on these ferrite cores, as you will very easily crack the brittle ferrite in two, completely destroying the adjuster and rendering it useless. Trying to extract such a broken core can take a long time and you will have to find another core from somewhere, so it is far better to heed this advice in the first place. If you find a core is stuck, *don't* try to force it round, instead carefully warm the core with the tip of a fine-point soldering iron bit; this will melt any oil around the core that has become waxy through the years. After removing the iron, quickly turn the core through a few full rotations, and you will find subsequent alteration far easier. I speak from bitter experience!

You'll also find many PA trimmers to have large screwdriver-shaped slots in them, though don't be tempted to use one. For example, if you use something like a six-inch long screwdriver, albeit with an insulated handle, on a metal trimmer capacitor in say the PA of a 70 cm transmitter, it will act as a lovely quarter-wave aerial and you'll be trying to tune the set for radiation from the screwdriver rather from subsequent stages!

If like many amateurs you don't already own a set of trimming tools (about £1–£2 for a small wallet containing a useful selection, from many electronic component and equipment dealers) then you may easily fabricate any as required for a 'one-off' tune-up. This may be done by filing down a matchstick or plastic knitting needle to suit the adjustments required in your particular equipment. Note that these may not last anywhere near a lifetime, but if one breaks during a tune-up then you can easily get the file out again! If you intend to align several equipments in the future, though, a set of the correct tools is a good investment. The ones to go for are those with flat adjustment ends; you will not need hexagonal adjusters for the equipment detailed here. You may find the larger flat-bladed tools have small metal end 'blades', with the remainder plastic, which will give longer wear and are quite acceptable but *only* for use on trimmer capacitors with metal adjustment slots.

Receiver Alignment

To align virtually any receiver, you will need a signal at the receiver frequency which can be modulated and continually varied in level. Readers with access to a suitable signal generator can stop reading this section straight away, as they will have all they need for complete receiver alignment. For others, such as those in the position I was in when I first started, please read on, as you certainly don't need access to all this expensive equipment to get your set on the air (although I must admit it does tend to make the job quicker!). To let you in on a secret, when as a teenager I first aligned a pair of PF1 pocketfones, I did it with the aid of only a cheap multimeter, an existing 2 m rig, and a filed down matchstick, in a basement flat 350 miles away from my home. All it needs is intuition . . . .

Off-Air Signals

For a strong signal, you can first make use of a nearby transmitter. I have known amateurs to drive up to a local 2 m or 70 cm repeater site to do this, for example. As the tuning progressed, driving away from the repeater in the direction of home provided the gradually reducing level of signal required. Another way is to enlist the help of a friendly local amateur who will radiate a signal for you and, by varying his power output and aerial beam heading, together with variation of your aerial system (from an outdoor affair down to a screwdriver or test lead plugged into the aerial socket), you will get a good range of signal level.

For 70 cm alignment, if you have a 2 m rig that is capable of transmitting on exactly one-third of your 70 cm receive frequency, this may be used to good effect by receiving the relatively weak 3rd harmonic. Again, by variation in aerials as well as high/low transmitter power switching you may gain a wide range of signal levels. Another possibility is if you have one of the commonly available low cost scanner receivers currently on the market. They invarably cover a wide range of frequencies, with their local oscillator normally running at the receive frequency minus the intermediate frequency. This local signal of course may be used for tuning purposes! To take an example, if you wish to align your set to 145.700 MHz, and your scanner has an IF of 10.7 MHz (look in your scanner's specification list for this), you simply key in 156.400 MHz into your scanner's keypad and you have an instant signal at the frequency you wish to align on.

In all cases, the final alignment may be done on a signal from a weak off-air source such as a distant repeater. Note that for final frequency setting, signals from repeaters are normally very accurate indeed (and need to be in order to comply with their licence regulations) as well as being regularly checked by the repeater group. I would hence be tempted to use these as a 'standard' rather than those from other off-air sources.

Transmitter Alignment

Here, some form of 50 ohm load to place on the aerial socket capable of handling the full transmit power is a necessity. This may be a commercial or home-built dummy load or, for the lower-power sets such as portables, a 47 ohm half watt carbon resistor works well. If you are constructing your own load, ensure you make it non-inductive; for example, don't use wirewound resistors even if these are the only types to handle the required power. Several smaller-wattage carbon resistors connected in parallel may of course be used, for example ten 470 ohm 2 watt carbon resistors arranged in a small 'cage' to keep lead lengths short, soldered onto the end of a short coax stub.

If you do need to use an aerial, make sure you do so in a manner so as not to cause interference to other users. For example, if you are aligning on several channels, use the 'quietest' of these for most of the tuning, only switching briefly to the others to trim the crystals to their required frequencies. Remember of course to identify your transmissions, and whatever you do don't align 'on air' to the input frequency of your busy local repeater or Raynet channel, except of course when finally checking performance with a previously arranged QSO, you may find you have few friends to talk to once your set is finally aligned!

Power Measurement

You will need some form of relative power indication to see how you are doing, although this need not be accurate in terms of actual power output level except for letting you know exactly what you're getting out. A small diode probe fed from a high level (e.g. 1 k–10 k) resistor coupled to the ends of your dummy load resistor arrangement. Alternatively, a tunable wavemeter (as we all must have to comply with our licence requirements) or a field strength meter may be used, again to give a relative indication of output power. I have often found the cheap in-line SWR meters with an adjustable 'sensitivity' control to be very useful. As the tuning progresses, the meter sensitivity may be decreased as required to

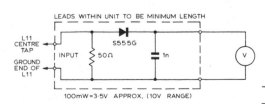

Simple-to-make power indicator for low power portable transmitter alignment.

RF field strength indicator.

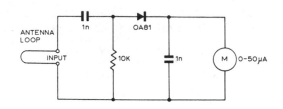

achieve a good deflection throughout most stages of the final power amplifier alignment.

Frequency and Deviation

To set your transmitter frequency, an on-air check with a friendly local amateur can be very effective, more so if he has a centre-zero facility on his S-meter so he can 'home' you in very accurately. Alternatively, if you or he have an SSB or CW rig, tuning to the required frequency on this followed by an adjustment of the appropriate crystal trimmer on the rig you are aligning for 'zero beat' will also provide a useful indication, allowing you to get spot-on accuracy. Don't be tempted to just adjust the trimmer until it 'sounds right' on another FM receiver, although this could be a useful starting point you could be up to several kHz off frequency.

For deviation adjustment, again an on-air check may be used to advantage. If you are setting up the transceiver to a local repeater frequency, after initial adjustment a further station in 'simplex' range can quickly switch between the repeater input and output frequencies while you shout a very loud 'four' or whatever into the microphone, to make sure you are exactly as 'loud' on the input as you are on the output. Again, many repeaters have their deviations set up very accurately, and limit any overdeviation received on the input frequency to 5 kHz at the output. If you find you are continually dropping out of the repeater squelch on peaks of modulation, and you have made sure you are accurately on frequency (one of the causes of this effect, combined with distortion), you will no doubt be overdeviating. Some repeaters also superimpose a 'pip' on your audio when reproduced on the output frequency when the input deviation is 'well over' the 5 kHz mark.

Professional Test Equipment

If you have access to test equipment such as a frequency counter, RF power meter, signal generator and modulation meter then by all means do use them. Your re-tuning and conversion projects will then be that much quicker as well as possibly giving a better 'spot-on' performance. If you are unfamiliar with the use of these, and especially if you are loaning someone's test gear, then do make sure

Test equipment in use.

you know how to use it! For instance, never connect your transmitter aerial socket to the input of a frequency counter, as soon as you press the PTT you will destroy the counter input stages. Also, it is wise to adopt sensible precautions, such as when tuning the receiver stages with a signal generator connected, remove the microphone from its socket, if possible, to prevent you accidentally transmitting into that. The moral here is that, if in doubt, get someone to help you, preferably the owner of the test gear.

If you are friendly with your local PMR dealer, one good final check is to take your finally-tuned set along to test on one of the standard PMR 'test sets' that occupy virtually every workshop. These are a combined piece of do-everything electronics, which are virtually indestructible in normal use, i.e. it would be difficult to blow one up. Within seconds you will see the receiver sensitivity, transmitter power, frequency error, and deviation. At the larger or specialized radio rallies, you will often find a 'transceiver clinic' is held, often using such a test set, with free supervised use being available for visitors.

4 MOBILE EQUIPMENT

THE WESTMINSTER SERIES

Westminsters appear in both remote and dash mount versions. The dash mount is ideal as a local club net or repeater/Raynet monitor, of course, although a little large for car mounting nowadays. The remote mount version is superb for fitting in your boot or under your seat out of the way, linked to a small control box under your dash, with volume, squelch, and channel controls on it. This also makes it much more resistant to theft. My last car was broken into twice by thieves about ten years ago after the radio gear, the first time the boot was crowbarred open, the airhorns and headlamps went on and off from the alarm system, but in the panic the thieves were foiled by my three boot mount Westminsters chained in the car.

The second time, a thief got into the interior and thought a control box was the radio; again he didn't hang about and went with nothing. You should be able to pick up a second hand Pye Westminster for anything from 25p to £15 depending upon frequency band and condition, but make sure you know what you are buying. The Westminster is a range of equipments, AM and FM, ranging from 32.5 MHz up to 470 MHz, a 68 MHz AM set looking absolutely identical to a 145 MHz FM set from the outside, apart from the serial number plate.

Frequency Bands
There have been seven frequency ranges commonly made:

32.5 MHz–42 MHz H Band FM Remote mount
42 MHz–54 MHz G Band FM Remote mount
68 MHz–88 MHz E Band AM/FM, Dash/Remote mount
132 MHz–156 MHz B Band AM/FM, Dash/Remote mount
148 MHz–174 MHz A Band AM/FM, Dash/Remote mount
405 MHz–440 MHz T Band FM, Remote mount
440 MHz–470 MHz U Band FM, Remote mount

The G band model is ideal for 6 m FM, in fact several amateurs in my area use these for general nattering on the band. Note that many of these are manufactured with sub-tone circuitry fitted to an elongated case. However, this is easily disconnected if required.

There is no truth to the rumours that the author has cornered the market in surplus Westminsters!

Both A and B band sets will tune to 2 m, the A band set being the more common. At the time of writing, several amateurs use AM on 4 m, hence details are given for the W15AM and the high power W30AM transceiver for this band, these are plentiful in supply and are often available at 'give-away' prices. For UHF use, both T and U band versions tune to 70 cm reasonably well, although to achieve optimum performance on receive it is important to obtain crystals on the correct side injection.

Identification and Selection

The usual set will have "W15****" marked on its plate, together with its original frequency. If the riveted plate has been removed then leave well alone! Following the "W15" will be an AM or FM, self explanatory, followed by 'B' or 'D', signifying Boot (remote) mount or Dash mount respectively. Another set you may come across is the LW15FM, which is actually a system 3 radiophone but, apart from having extra digital circuitry comprised in its elongated case, it is identical to the A band W15FMB, and will make an ideal 2 m transceiver. It has both internal and external multi-way connectors and, if you plug a standard control box into the internal connector, you'll find you bypass the digital circuits completely.

The final identification letter on the plate will, if appropriate, (VHF sets) indicate the channel spacing, and hence filter width:

N – 50 kHz spacing, +/– 15 kHz filters
V – 25 kHz spacing, +/– 7.5 kHz filters
S – 12.5 kHz spacing, +/– 3.75 kHz filters

Look out for a V spacing set if you want it for 2 m, or alternatively an S spacing set for 12.5 kHz channel use, but you will suffer from adjacent channel interference with an N spacing set (fairly old and hence rare). Many of the very early UHF Westminsters were made with 50 kHz channel spacing in mind. If you do end up with an unsuitable set then Garex Ltd., amongst others, can sell you suitable filters to do a swap with. However, please don't be tempted to buy an AM set hoping to convert it to FM – it just isn't worth it unless you're prepared for a lot of work. If you've already got an AM set, then economics dictate that, with surplus sets being so cheap, it is often cheaper to throw the AM set in the bin; sorry but that's how it is! You may see a number at the end of the equipment code, this is the number of channels the set is capable of being used on, normally 1, 3, 6, or 10. Note that all control box channel switches, if fitted, switch 10 channels but these may not all be provided for inside the transceiver. A look inside the covers is a wise move before purchase though, to see how many crystal positions are available on the printed circuit boards, two per channel. Although you may not need it for more than one channel at first, you may wish to fit a simplex channel or club net channel in the future.

Boot and Dash Mounts

The circuitry used in the equipment is virtually the same between dash and boot mounts, the difference being only in the control. A multiway connector on the boot mount connects to an 'umbilical'

Boot-mounted Westminsters, VHF (top), UHF (bottom).

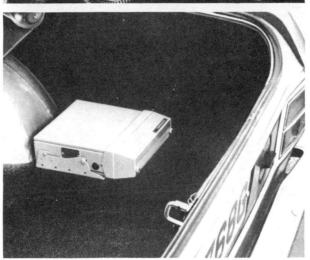

control cable terminated in a small box with the controls, two models of control box have been made but with identical circuitry. Do however make sure you get a box *and* cable if you buy a boot mount set. Often, installers remove the sets from cars along with the control box, but leave the cable due to difficulties of removal. Don't worry too much if a microphone or speaker doesn't come with the set, as any 3–8 ohm speaker and 500–2000 ohm dynamic microphone will work, although the originals will usually give the best performance. The microphone plug is a five pin 270 degree DIN, commonly available, although some dash mount models have the mic cable permanently wired in. The power lead with plug is sometimes missing also, and many amateurs have tried in vain to wire one up without the correct information. A 7-pin Plessey-type free socket is required; for negative earth DC use the positive feed connects to pin 1, the negative feed to pin 7, and internal to the free socket, two links are required, these linking between pins 2 and 3, and between 4 and 5. I would advise fitting a five amp fuse in line with your DC cable.

I will first describe the VHF FM range, then the VHF AM Westminster suitable for 4 m AM, and finally the W15U UHF version.

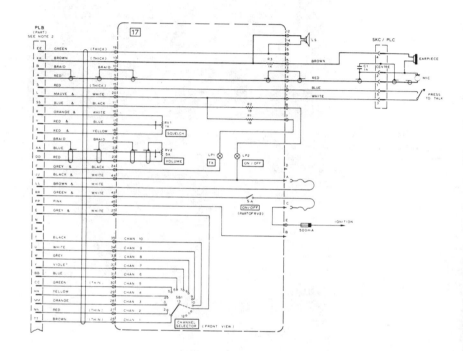

Control unit wiring diagram.

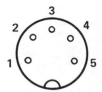

1—MICROPHONE LIVE
2—MICROPHONE SCREEN
3—PTT COMMON −VE
4—EARPHONE AUDIO
5—PTT MAKE

**VIEW FROM WIRING SIDE OF PLUG
NOTE NON-STANDARD NUMBERING**

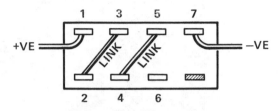

**VIEW FROM WIRING SIDE OF PLUG,
IE: FRONT OF SET CONNECTIONS**

Microphone and power plug connections.

THE VHF FM WESTMINSTER

Crystals

The crystal frequencies required are:

$$\text{RX CRYSTAL} = \frac{\text{RX FREQ(MHz)} - 10.7}{1} \text{ MHz} \quad \begin{matrix} (42-54 \text{ MHz}) \\ (6\text{m}) \end{matrix}$$

$$= \frac{\text{RX FREQ (MHz)} - 10.7}{2} \text{ MHz} \quad \begin{matrix} (68-88 \text{ MHz}) \\ (4\text{m}) \end{matrix}$$

$$= \frac{\text{RX FREQ(MHz)} - 10.7}{3} \text{ MHz} \quad \begin{matrix} (132-174 \text{ MHz}) \\ (2\text{m}) \end{matrix}$$

$$\text{TX CRYSTAL} = \frac{\text{TX FREQ(MHz)}}{12} \text{ MHz} \quad \begin{matrix} (42-54 \text{ MHz}) \\ (6\text{m}) \end{matrix}$$

$$= \frac{\text{TX FREQ(MHz)}}{24} \text{ MHz} \quad \begin{matrix} (68-88 \text{ MHz}) \\ (4\text{m}) \end{matrix}$$

$$= \frac{\text{TX FREQ(MHz)}}{36} \text{ MHz} \quad \begin{matrix} (132-174 \text{ MHz}) \\ (2\text{m}) \end{matrix}$$

**Underside layout—
Dash mount W15FM**

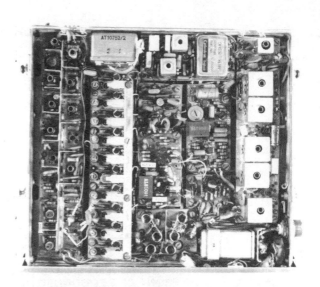

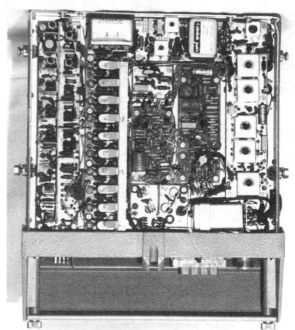

**Underside layout—
Remote mount
W15FM**

Both crystals are HC6/U size, the commercial specifications of these vary depending upon use but if the 'Westminster' is quoted when ordering crystals that in itself should be totally sufficient.

Receiver Alignment

First of all, connect your DC supply and plug in a suitable speaker.

Take care not to short the speaker connections out as this will often destroy one or both of the 40310 audio power transistors in the receiver AF amplifier. Because the receiver switching bandwidth is fairly narrow, it is useful to tune the receiver on the channel nearest the centre of your desired operational frequency range, although this is only important if you need to operate on, for example on 2 m, a repeater channel as well as a frequency on the lower part of the band.

Connect your multimeter negative to the negative supply line, and positive to Board 5 TP1. On the centre channel, using your ferrite adjuster trimming tool, tune L1 and L3 both for maximum. Then transfer to TP2 and tune L4 for maximum, retuning L1, L3, and L4 for absolute maximum on TP2. That completes the crystal oscillator multiplier alignment.

Now turn the set over and align the front end for best sensitivity on a received signal. First of all, tune the appropriate crystal trimmer until your received signal is audible, then fine tune this if possible for minimum distortion on a modulated signal. An initial RF tuning aid is TP1 on board 3, with a strong received signal tune coils L5, T2, L4, T1, L3 and L1, in that order, on the front end board (board 1) for maximum voltage on TP1, reducing the received signal as necessary to keep the reading at around 0.7 V if possible. Final tuning is carried out on a weak signal, again tuning L1, L3, T1, L4, T2 and L5 on board 1 for best quieting, although you may find that only L1 in this case makes any significant difference to the sensitivity. If the set has been

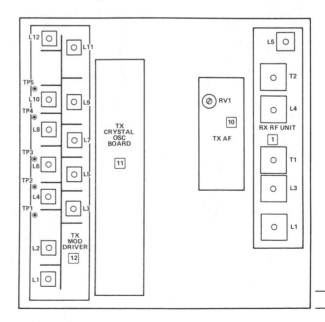

Underside alignment points.

used in service before, then the I.F. and squelch circuitry will have been aligned and I recommend that you leave well alone.

Netting the receiver onto frequency may initially be done by tuning the coil adjacent to the respective crystal for best (least distorted) reception as detailed, a more accurate check however may now be done by connecting your multimeter to Board 3 TP3, and tuning for zero voltage. The more enthusiastic amongst us may even fit a centre- zero meter to this point if desired, for use in a base station mode.

A typical receiver sensitivity is in the order of 0.35 uV pd for 12 dB SINAD, possibly a little deaf by today's standards but certainly useful for most operation with local signals, and certainly adequate for most uses as a dedicated packet radio station.

Topside layout—Dash mount W15FM

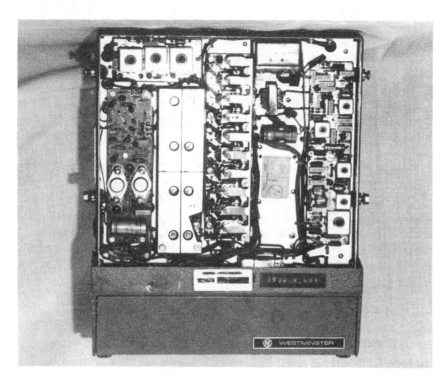

Topside layout—Remote mount W15FM

Transmitter Alignment

Connect your multimeter negative lead to the power supply negative, and set the meter to a voltage range of 10 V, and connect your power meter and load to the aerial connector. Key the PTT, checking you hear the slight click of the mechanical aerial change-over relay, and connect the meter positive lead to TP1 on board 12. Remember to keep your TX keyed whenever taking readings. With your ferrite core adjuster, tune L1 and L2 both for maximum, re-tuning as required to give absolute maximum, then tune L3 for minimum reading. Transfer the meter positive lead to TP2 and tune L4 and then L3 for maximum, then L5 for minimum (miss this step out on G band, i.e. 6 m sets, as L4, L5 and TP2 are not fitted). Now transfer to TP3 and tune L6 and then L5 (L3, G band) for maximum, then L7 for minimum. Connect to TP4 and tune L8 then L7 for maximum, then L9 for minimum.

G band sets only Transfer your multimeter to TP5, and tune L10 for maximum, this will read around 0.5 V. Now on the PA board, on the opposite side of the chassis, connect to TP1 and tune L11 and L12 on the driver board for maximum. Then transfer back to TP5 on the driver board, and tune L10 and then L9 for maximum, then back to TP1 on the PA board tuning L11 and L12 again for maximum. That completes the driver tune-up, we now skip the next bit and proceed straight onto the PA alignment.

E, B and A band sets only (i.e. 2m/4m). We use this driver stage as a low power transmitter, but for G band sets skip this and go straight onto the PA alignment. Disconnect the coax at the end of the board, next to L11, and feed the RF into our power meter, terminated in a 50 ohm load, a 47 ohm half or quarter watt carbon resistor should be suitable here if nothing else is available. At this point it is, of course, safe to leave the TX PA disconnected from a load as we shall not be

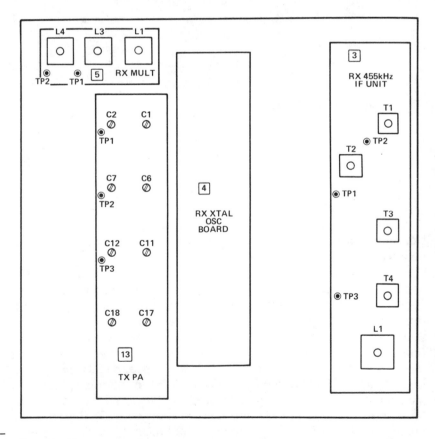

Topside alignment points.

generating power from it. On the driver board, with the TX keyed tune L10, L11, and L12 in that order for maximum power (around 1/4 watt), then re-tune L10, L9, L11 and L12 for absolute maximum. Unkey the transmitter and switch the DC power off, then re-connect the coax we removed to link the PA back into circuit.

PA Alignment

Here you will need a flat-bladed trimming tool, and I find it useful to have a pair of these in practice, using one in each hand to tune the pairs of capacitors together for absolute maximum rather than using one adjuster and alternating back and forth. Switch the set back on, and from now on just keep the TX keyed only for as long as is required to take a reading, to save the PA stages trying to generate power when not correctly tuned. Connect your multimeter positive lead to TP1 on the PA board, and tune C1 and C2 for maximum. Then transfer to TP2 and tune C6 and C7 alternately for maximum reading again. For E, B and A band sets only, transfer to TP3, and tune C11 and C12 for maximum. By now, you should see some RF indicated on your power meter connected to the aerial socket. Tune C17 and C18 (or C11 and C12 in the case of G band sets) for maximum indicated power into the 50 ohm load, then go back to the preceding trimmers and tune again in pairs until you obtain the maximum possible RF power output, this should be in the order of 12–18 W, nominally 15 W.

Now you can accurately set each crystalled channel onto frequency, using the small ceramic trimmer adjacent to the relevant crystal. RV1 on the TX AF board, (board 10, both clearly marked) sets the peak deviation, mic gain is pre-set and not adjustable.

Receiver Improvements

The sensitivity may be improved by fitting a simple pre-amp, several proprietary makes being available such as those from Cirkit, Wood and Douglas, and a range from Garex. The front end stages may, however, be modified to achieve better sensitivity without significantly degrading the strong signal handling capability by replacing TR3 and TR5 (2N3819's) on the front end board with J310 transistors. The transistor drain current must be optimised to gain the greatest benefit, this is done by changing the values of R6 and R14 (120R originally) to achieve 10 mA current through them as measured with your multimeter. A typical improvement of around 6 dB increase in sensitivity is achieved as a result.

Packet Radio Use

The Westminster on 2 m is a very popular packet radio 'stand alone' rig amongst amateurs in the UK. Coupled to a TNC, it makes a useful

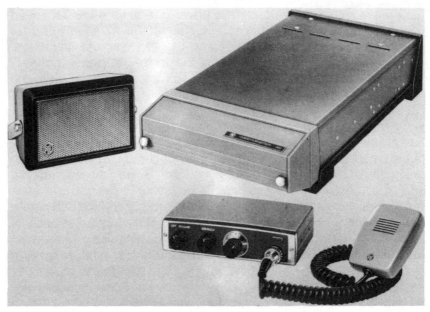

The W30AM may be identified from the ventilation slots at the rear of the lid.

low-cost station allowing the main transceiver to be freed for other uses. To achieve better interfacing with the TNC, using the 'flat' audio inputs and outputs from this, you may wish to make the following modifications:

TX Audio Inject non pre-emphasized transmit audio from your TNC through a 68K resistor and 10nF capacitor wired in series, to the base of TR3 on the TX AF PCB, Board 10. Silence the previous stages by placing a wire link across pins 3 and 4, the mic connections. This bypasses the mic pre-emphasis and clipper stages.

RX Audio Remove the 0.22 uf capacitor C32 on the RX 455 kHz IF PCB, Board 3, replacing this with a 1k resistor and 47 nF capacitor wired in parallel. This removes the receiver de-emphasis. Take audio to the non de-emphasised RX AF input on your TNC from across the volume control potentiometer, or from the RX AF PCB, board 8, at pin 8 with ground at pin 9, you'll find approx. 2 V peak/peak at this point. Do not take audio out from pin 5 on this PCB, the audio input, as this point is current driven rather than voltage driven.

THE W15AM AND W30AM FOR 4 M

W15AM is the most popular. This gives around 8 W output, and there

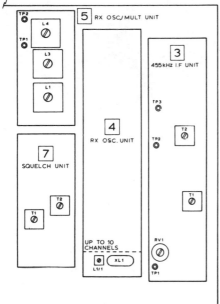

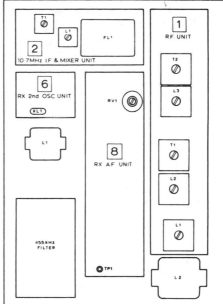

AM Westminster oscillator alignment points.

AM Westminster receiver front end alignment points.

have recently also been a large number of W30AMB sets released onto the market. These are almost identical but with the addition of a quick heat QQZ0640 single valve amplifier in the PA. The power, microphone and control box connections are the same as those of the FM series, but note that the microphone element itself is different. For AM use, it has a rising response with frequency, and may be identified by having a large number of holes in a star formation on the front of the insert, as opposed to the FM insert with its three small holes.

Crystals

The required crystals are HC6/u size, the frequencies required being given by:

$$\text{RX XTAL FREQ} = \frac{\text{RX FREQ} - 10.7\,\text{MHz}}{2}$$

$$\text{TX XTAL FREQ} = \frac{\text{TX FREQ}}{2}$$

Receiver Alignment

Insert your transmit and receive crystals, making sure you get them

AM Westminster initial transmitter alignment points.

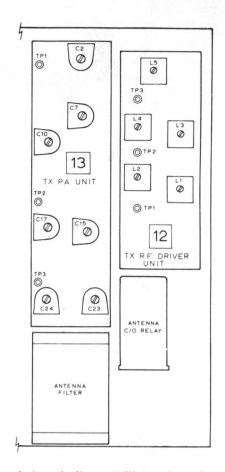

the correct way round in view of the similar oscillator boards, connect your set up to DC power and switch on. Connect the negative lead of your multimeter to the negative voltage supply (not the set chassis, this is not negative) and set the range to the 2.5 V DC scale. Connect the positive multimeter lead to TP1 on the RX Multiplier board, and with your ferrite core trimming tool, tune L1 for maximum reading, then L3 for minimum. Transfer the positive multimeter lead to TP2 and tune L4, then L3, then L1 all for maximum. Disconnect the meter positive lead, set the meter to a sensitive current range such as 50 uA, and connect the positive lead to TP3 on the 455 kHz IF board. Now we need to receive an off-air signal, while doing this tune the ferrite core adjacent to your receive crystal to ensure reception on the correct frequency. The squelch on an AM set may make little difference to the background noise with no aerial connected, so ensure this is rotated to its fully open position when tuning a weak signal. While receiving your off-air signal, tune T2, L3, T1, L2, and L1 on the RX front end for best reception, indicated by maximum meter reading, keeping this below 30 uA by reducing the level of signal received accordingly. Re-tune as required for the absolute best sensitivity, checking and adjusting as required the appropriate crystal trimmer to ensure co-channel reception. The coils on the 10.7 MHz and 455 kHz IF boards should not need re-tuning, so leave well alone.

Transmitter Alignment

If yours is a W30AM, then prior to keying the transmitter, set the 'Tune/Tx' switch to 'Tune', this avoids over-dissipation in the valve amplifier on tune-up. Set your multimeter again to the 2.5 V DC range, connect the negative lead to the DC supply negative (not chassis), and the positive lead to TP2 on the TX driver board. Keeping the mic keyed, or the TX button pressed on the front of a remote mount set, tune L1 and L2 for maximum reading. Transfer the multimeter positive lead to TP3, and tune L3 and L4 again for maximum, repeating as required for absolute maximum.

W15AM The following now applies to the W15AM. W30AM owners skip to the next paragraph. Connect your multimeter lead to TP1 on the PA board, and tune L5 the driver board and then C2 on the PA for maximum. You will need a flat-bladed trimming tool to align the PA capacitors. Transfer to TP2, tuning C7 and C10 on the PA board for maximum reading, then transfer to TP3 and tune C15 and C17 again for maximum. By now, you should start to see a bit of RF power indicated, and tune C23 and C24 for maximum. Then go back and re-tune C2, C7, C10, C15, C17, C23 and C24 in that order for absolute maximum, then adjust the crystal trimmer for accurate frequency netting.

W30AM For W30AM users, the tune-up is a little more tricky, but you'll get around 30 W output for your trouble. Switch to the 2.5 V DC range on your multimeter, and connect the negative lead to the DC supply negative, and the positive multimeter lead to TP1 on the TX PA board. Tune L5 on the driver board, and C1 and C2 on the PA board for maximum, then transfer to TP2 and tune C6 and C7 also for maximum. Now disconnect your multimeter leads, set it to the 250 uA range and connect the positive multimeter lead to chassis and the negative lead to TP3 on the valve PA unit. Tune C11 and then C13 both on the TX PA board, for maximum reading, repeating as required to gain the absolute maximum. Now disconnect your multimeter leads, switch to the 50 uA range, and connect the positive lead to TP1 and the negative lead to TP2, both on the valve PA unit.

Initially set the vanes of C17 fully apart (minimum capacity) and

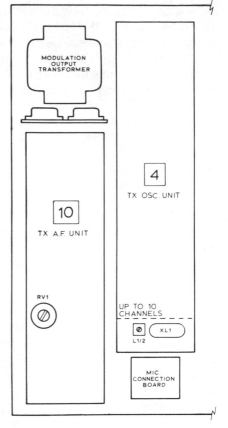

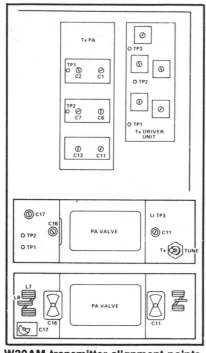

W30AM transmitter alignment points.

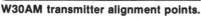

W15AM modulation and oscillator alignment points.

tune C16 for minimum deflection on the meter. By now your RF power meter should be reading, so tune C17 for maximum indicated power. Now it is safe to switch the 'TX/Tune' switch back to TX so do this, and you'll find your RF power increases nicely. Replace the set's bottom cover, and re-adjust C16 slightly as required to give a minimum reading on your multimeter – this should be around 12–20 uA – then re-tune C17 for maximum RF power. To obtain the absolute best performance, I would advise that you go over the final stages of PA alignment again, also you'll find that varying the positioning of L8 to L7 on the PA, coupled with realignment of C17, will give varying maximum output, but be careful not to go above 30 W output or you'll run out of modulation power. That's it, check your crystal trimmer for co-channel accuracy and you're finished.

The transmit modulation level on both versions is set by RV1 on the TX AF board, this should already be set at around the appropriate level but may be adjusted either way as required from off-air reports, being careful to ensure overmodulation doesn't occur.

The UHF Westminster.

THE W15U UHF WESTMINSTER

These are seen at rallies for anything from £5 upwards, and represent an ideal way to have many pleasant informal chats on 70 cm without the expense of a more sophisticated transceiver. The vast majority of UHF Westminsters are remote mounted, however a very small number were manufactured as a dash-mount version, the circuitry and alignment details being similar. They draw about 2 Amps on transmit from your DC supply and commonly give around 4 W output, although transmitter circuitry has varied slightly in the past. On receive, expect around 0.5 uV for 12 dB SINAD, although this is not very sensitive by present day standards and I will show how it may easily be improved.

Crystals

Sort out what frequency you want it on, by asking the chaps at the local club or by taking a look at a repeater list to identify your local 'box', as most activity is very localized. Once this is done, calculate the crystal frequencies if necessary according to the formulae:

$$\text{TX XTAL (MHz)} = \frac{\text{TRANSMIT FREQUENCY (MHz)}}{32}$$

$$\text{RX XTAL (MHz)} = \frac{(\text{RECEIVE FREQUENCY} + 10.7\,\text{MHz})}{36}$$

The crystal can size is HC6/u, and quote the UHF Westminster when ordering to ensure the correct loading etc. is supplied, the commercial crystal specification in this case being T40. There is one point that many amateurs have fallen down on. Some crystal firms state they supply the correct crystals 'ex-stock'; if purchasing from these firms then *ensure* you quote the correct CRYSTAL frequencies. The reason for this is that the UHF Westminster is made in two frequency ranges, T and U band, the latter usually appearing on the surplus market in this country. However the receiver crystal multiplier is exactly the same between ranges, with the same overall tuning range. On T band positive side injection is used, on U band negative side injection is used, and by trying to pull the many stages of this board down in frequency could possibly lead you to a few problems. Don't be fobbed off by the supplier saying "Oh, yes, your set is 'high UHF band' so you need these crystals", as I was told a while ago, this is totally incorrect.

Receiver Alignment

Set your multimeter to the 2.5 V DC range, with the negative lead connected to supply negative (not the chassis, this is not negative). Ensure you have the correct frequency crystals plugged in, and if aligning for several channels switch to the one nearest the centre of the total frequency range. Switch the set on, and make sure that you hear noise from the speaker when opening the receiver squelch using the rotary squelch control. Connect the multimeter positive lead to board TP1, and using your ferrite adjuster tool tune L3 and L4 both for maximum voltage reading. Transfer to TP2 and tune L6 and L7 again for maximum. Transfer to TP3, and tune L9 and L10 for maximum. Now we go onto the front end module (Module 16), the large silver-plated block with several metal adjusters sticking out of it. If you have a diode probe, this may be used on the junction of R7 and C16, tuning C18 on Module 16, and C25 on Board 5, both for maximum. If not, you will need to tune these later for best received signal.

Now we need a strongish signal on your crystalled frequency: first of all, net your crystal onto frequency by tuning the trimmer

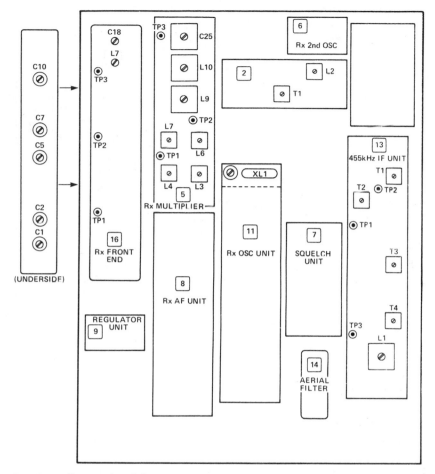

Receiver alignment points.

adjacent to the appropriate crystal for best reception (least distortion) on the received signal. You may like to monitor the voltage on board 3 TP3 while receiving a signal you know is spot on frequency, setting the crystal trimmer for 0 volts reading, this will net it precisely. If a diode probe was not available earlier, adjust C18 on module 16 and C25 on board 5 for best quieting signal, reducing signal level as necessary.

On the front end board, module 16, adjust C10, C7, C2, C1, and L7 for best quieting signal, reducing signal strength as required. Then re-adjust C18, and C25 on board 5, again for best quieting. Go through the procedure again to ensure the best sensitivity possible, doing the final test on a very weak signal. The I.F. and squelch stages

Transmitter alignment points.

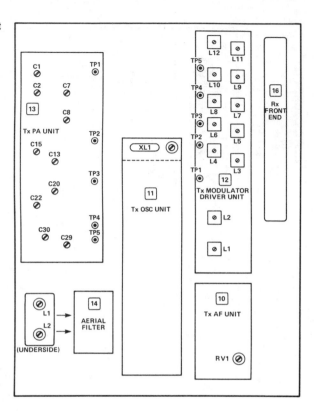

will of course have already been aligned if the set has come out of commercial service, so there is no need to adjust anything here.

Transmitter Alignment
Switch to your selected crystal frequency, and connect the negative lead of your multimeter to the supply negative, switch to the 2.5 V DC range, and connect its positive lead to TP1 on Board 12. Throughout the transmitter alignment, you must of course keep the TX keyed; you will find a handy push button for this purpose on the front panel of the set. Key the TX and carefully tune L1 and L2 for maximum voltage reading. If you have difficulty in getting a 'peak', then try tuning L1 for a maximum diode probe reading at the junction of C1/L1, and L2 for maximum at the junction of C5/L2. Back to TP1 with the multimeter, and tune L3 for minimum, then re-tune L1 and L2 for absolute maximum.

Then transfer to TP2, and tune L4 for maximum reading, then L3 for maximum, then L5 for minimum. Transfer to TP3, tune L6 for maximum, then L5 for maximum, and then L7 for minimum. Transfer to TP4, tune L8 for maximum, L7 for maximum, then L9 for minimum. Transfer to TP5, and tune L10 for maximum, then L9 for maximum, and finally L11 for minimum. By now, if you have an adjacent 70 cm receiver such as a handheld, you will be able to hear a signal on your crystalled channel from your Westminster. You can take this opportunity of giving the relevant crystal trimmer a quick adjustment to give you the best received signal (least distortion on speech modulation).

Now for the power amplifier. There have been two types in common production, an early model with two output transistors or a later model with a single heavier-duty transistor, identified by the number of adjustment holes in the PA screen. Fit a 50 ohm load to the aerial socket with your power meter in line. For adjustments on the PA board you will need a flat screwdriver-blade shaped tool, again made from a non-metallic material.

Early Model PA

Initially set C14, C18, and C27 to minimum capacity (vanes unmeshed), and C6, C8, C15, C22, C23 and C28 to mid capacity (vanes half-meshed). Set your multimeter to a low DC current setting, preferably around 250 uA, and connect the positive lead to TP5 and the negative lead to TP1, both on board 13 (the PA stage). Tune L11 and L12 on board 12 for maximum, then L1 on the PA board for maximum. Transfer the negative lead to TP2 and tune C6 and C8 for maximum reading. Transfer the negative lead again to TP3, tuning C14 for maximum. Transfer the negative lead to TP4 and tune C18 for maximum. Hopefully by now you should be able to see some indication of output power, so tune L1 and L2 on the aerial filter (module 13) for maximum; you will need a pair of small pliers for these adjusters. You may find a diode probe or adjacent receiver with S-meter useful if you cannot get a reading straight away. Then tune C22 and C23 for maximum on TP4 – you will find these will both tune at around the same capacitance each – and then re-tune C18 for maximum. Transfer back to TP3, tuning C15 and then C14 for maximum. Back again to TP2 and re-tune C6 and C8 for maximum. Now we can start tuning for maximum power indicated from the aerial socket. Monitoring the output power, tune C28, then L1 and L2 on the aerial filter, then C28 and C29 for maximum power.

Late Model PA

This one is a bit less tricky! Initially set all trimmers to their mid-capacity setting (vanes half-meshed). Set your multimeter to a low d.c. current setting, around 250 uA is ideal, and connect the positive lead to TP5 on the PA unit, and the negative lead to TP1. Tune L11 and L12 on the driver unit, board 12 for maximum, then on the PA board tune C1 and C2 again for maximum. Transfer the negative

**Early model
transmitter power
amplifier unit.**

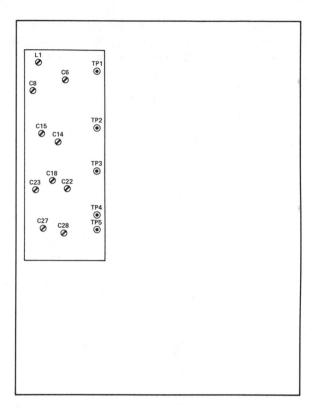

lead to TP2 and tune C7 and C8 for maximum. Transfer the negative lead again to TP3 and tune C13 for maximum, and C20 for minimum. On the aerial filter (module 14), use a small pair of pliers and tune L1 and L2 for maximum on the output power meter, (see above for a few hints if in difficulties here). Now tune C20 for maximum output power. Going back to TP3, tune C15, C13, C8, and C7 for maximum current. Re-tune L1 and L2 on the aerial filter for maximum output, also C22 and C20 again for maximum. You may repeat the PA tuning procedure to get the last possible milliwatt out if desired.

All that now remains is to set up the frequency if not already done so, adjusting the small ceramic trimmer capacitor adjacent to the relevant crystal with a flat-bladed adjuster. The peak deviation should be set to 5 kHz, by adjusting RV1 on board 10. With 25 kHz channel spacing ex-commercial sets, this will already be set to near the required level, but very early equipments may have been used on 50 kHz channel spacing with 15 kHz deviation and will sound very distorted unless you turn the deviation down, these are fairly rare nowadays though. Note that this is a peak deviation adjustment only, mic gain being fixed.

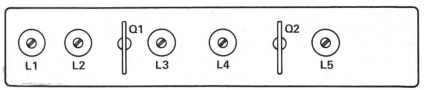

INTERIOR VIEW

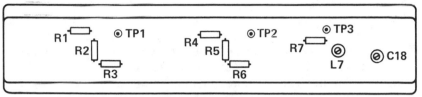

BOTTOM VIEW

Receiver front end component layout.

UHF Receiver Improvements

At this point you will have a working set, but you may find the receiver a bit lacking in sensitivity when compared to the latest equipment available, although in the majority of cases it will be perfectly satisfactory. So, please, try it first! If you would like to improve the receiver sensitivity by a few dB, you may like to perform the following modifications which have been successfully implemented by myself and other amateurs on several W15U sets in the past, improving the receive performance from around 0.4 uV pd to typically 0.25 uV pd for 12 dB SINAD.

1 Remove the front end (module 16) metal cover, and add 1/3rd of a turn to each of the five large coils, using thick (12 SWG) copper wire, preferably silver plated.
2 Replace the two BF180 transistors mounted on the inner screens with BFY90 transistors, soldering the BFY90 screen connections to the metal screen of the module. Keep the leads as short as possible.
3 Replace R1 and R4 with 12 k resistors.
4 Replace R2 and R5 with 4k7 resistors.
5 Replace R3 and R6 with 820R resistors.
6 Add a 2uF2 16 vw capacitor across the supply connections adjacent to R7.

Fit the cover back on, ensuring the screws are tight and re-tune the front end stages for best performance as described in 'receiver alignment'.

Repeater Conversion

The W15U has the capability of operating as a single-unit UHF repeater. There is, in fact, a talk-through version made, hence you will see on the front panel there is space for an extra BNC connector. Fit one here, and wire the transmitter aerial filter output direct to its adjacent socket, the other socket direct to the receiver front end. You will now have a spare co-axial aerial relay to use for your aerial system. Disconnect the wire from pin 7 on board 9, the voltage regulator unit. This is the mute line that inhibits the receiver on transmit, and will allow simultaneous TX/RX. Receive audio may be taken to the repeater control logic from the top of the volume control, with TX audio being fed directly to the mic connection. Good RF isolation is already provided in the W15U by the inherent screening between TX and RX stages, these being built on opposite sides of the main chassis. TX keying may be performed with an open collector NPN transistor from mic connection No. 3 down to 0V. RX squelch output may be taken from pin 9, board 9, which goes to 1.1V on squelch open, and 9.0V when squelch is closed.

THE EUROPA SERIES

The Europa is a reasonably compact dashmount transceiver, with a built-in speaker on the right hand side of the facia and two side-mounted rotary controls. It is easily separated from the similar Pye 'Motafone' by the Europa's elongated front panel housing a plug-in module at the left hand side of the facia. You may find this has a blank unit installed, as shown in the photograph, or alternately it may be fitted with a tone facility unit housing various buttons and indicators. If you find the latter then don't worry as it may easily be linked out of circuit as I will show later.

Identification
On the serial number plate found on the rear panel of the set, following the 'Equipment Type' you will see:

MF5FM   8W VHF set, 3 or 6 channel
MF25FM   25W VHF set, 6 channel
MF5U   5W UHF set, 3 channel

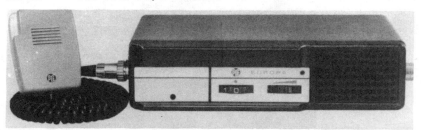

The Europa.

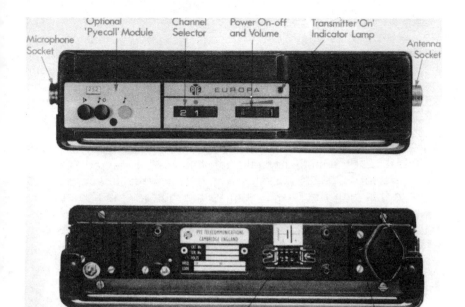

Microphone Socket · Optional 'Pyecall' Module · Channel Selector · Power On-off and Volume · Transmitter 'On' Indicator Lamp · Antenna Socket

Mounting Cradle · Power Socket · External Loudspeaker Sockets

Front and rear views.

This will normally be followed by the frequency band code:

VHF: A   146–174 MHz
      B   132–156 MHz
      P   79–101 MHz
      E   68– 88 MHz

UHF: T   380–440 MHz
      U   440–470 MHz

Also, for VHF equipments, the channel spacing will be indicated by an 'S' for 12.5 kHz, and a 'V' for 25 kHz (20 kHz channel spacing models being made for export only), possibly followed also by a '3' or '6' to indicate 3 or 6 channel facility.

You will find the A and B band versions suitable for 2 m, the A band being the more commonly available of the two, and either the U or T band versions suitable for 70 cm with the U band model being the more common. The E band model is perfect for 4 m of course. The 'P' band Europa is a bit of a rarity, but it simply is not worthwhile attempting to 'convert' this due to the abundance of cheap A and U band sets on the market.

Channel Spacing

All UHF Europas employ 25 kHz channel spacing, making them suitable for current use on 70 cm. However the VHF sets may either be 12.5 kHz *or* 25 kHz sets, so do ensure you obtain a set to suit your needs. At the time of writing, the majority of usage is based on 25 kHz spacing, but proposals are afoot to possibly go to formal 12.5 kHz spacing on 2 m in the UK with corresponding changes in equipment parameters.

If you are in any doubt as to the spacing of your Europa, take a look inside at the metal crystal filter, this will be marked FC03233 (12.5 kHz) or FC03234 (25 kHz). It is however reasonably easy to replace this with the type to suit your requirements and surplus dealers may be able to supply the correct type. Apart from this filter, only slight realignment is required to change between the two in practice for most amateur needs.

Crystals

The required crystal frequencies are:

4 m: $\text{RX Xtal Freq (MHz)} = \dfrac{\text{RX Freq (MHz)} - 10.7}{8}$

$\text{TX Xtal Freq (MHz)} = \dfrac{\text{Tx Freq (MHz)}}{16}$

2 m: $\text{RX Xtal Freq (MHz)} = \dfrac{\text{RX Freq (MHz)} + 10.7}{12}$

$\text{TX Xtal Freq (MHz)} = \dfrac{\text{TX Freq (MHz)}}{16}$

70 cm $\text{RX Xtal Freq (MHz)} = \dfrac{\text{RX Freq (MHz)} + 10.7}{36}$

$\text{TX Xtal Freq (MHz)} = \dfrac{\text{TX Freq (MHz)}}{32}$

The crystal case size for the 3 channel set is HC6/u, and the smaller HC25/u for the six channel set. You will find crystals are available ex-stock on popular channels for the Europa from the usual suppliers, but if you need to order them specially you may find it handy to quote their specification type T25 (3 Chan. VHF.) or T80 (6 Chan. VHF), with T40 for UHF. Note the UHF crystals are identical to those used in the earlier Pye W15U UHF Westminster. It is

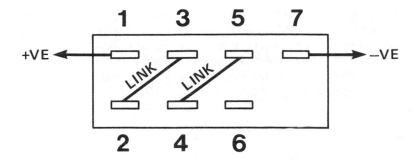

PYE EUROPA DC POWER PLUG WIRING (NEG. EARTH)

Connections, similar to the Westminster series.

physically possible to replace the crystal sockets in the 3 channel sets with those suitable for HC25/u crystals, but not vice-versa, so take care to order the correct crystal sizes for your needs.

Connections

The microphone connections are the standard 5-pin 270 deg. DIN plug, but note that TX PTT control is done by switching the + 10 V line between pin 3 and pin 5; if you are connecting a packet radio TNC to this then bear the polarity in mind.

Note that the receiver audio output is available on the two-pin socket on the rear of the set, but this is a floating line, so *do not* connect one of these to earth, as you could easily destroy the audio IC which is rather expensive to replace. If you need to connect an external speaker, make sure it has an impedance of greater than 6 ohms. If you wish to connect received audio to your TNC, link its audio input to PCB pins 12 (live) and 11 (Screen), this is the squelched audio feed to the volume control. If you require a 'busy' squelch line output, the collector of TR14 on the RX PCB of both VHF and UHF sets switches between 0.9 V (busy) and 8.4 V (no signal).

The 13.8 V DC connection uses a 7 pin Plessey type free socket, the connection details for this being similar to the Westminster series. I would recommend using a 5 A fuse in line with the MF5 sets, and a 10 A fuse in line with the MF25 set.

Opening Up

Remove the top lid of the equipment by removing the three screws at the rear of the case, then remove the three screws securing the PCB and hinge this upwards. Insert your crystals in their respective positions. Check that Pins 8 and 12 are linked on the facility socket on the TX board (pin 1 is at the left looking from the front of the set), either by a PCB link on a blanking board or by a wire link at the rear of the socket. If a tone option board is fitted here, I would recommend removing the board and fitting the appropriate link in its place.

VHF Alignment

Start by switching to the appropriate channel for your crystal, and connect your multimeter negative lead to the DC supply negative line. Switch to the 10 V DC position, and connect the positive lead to TP7. Tune the core of L10 for a 'dip' in the meter reading, re-adjusting carefully for minimum voltage reading. Now transfer the positive lead to TP8, and tune L11 and then L10 for maximum reading, re-tune again for absolute maximum and then tune L12 for minimum voltage. Transfer the positive lead to TP10, and tune first L13 and then L12 for maximum, then tune L16 for minimum. Transfer to TP6, and tune L17, then L16 for maximum, re-tuning again as required for absolute maximum. This completes the crystal multiplier alignment; now we go on to the RX front end.

Here we need to receive a signal at the aerial connection, so start by adjusting the relevant multi-turn crystal trimmer to ensure your crystal is on frequency, continuing until you are sure you are receiving the least distortion possible on a modulated signal. You may find it useful to open the receiver squelch whilst tuning, by adjusting RV1 which is the squelch preset control. On the large metal block front end assembly, short TP4 to the 10 V line, i.e. the

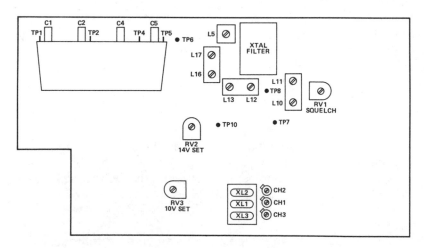

VHF Europa receiver alignment points.

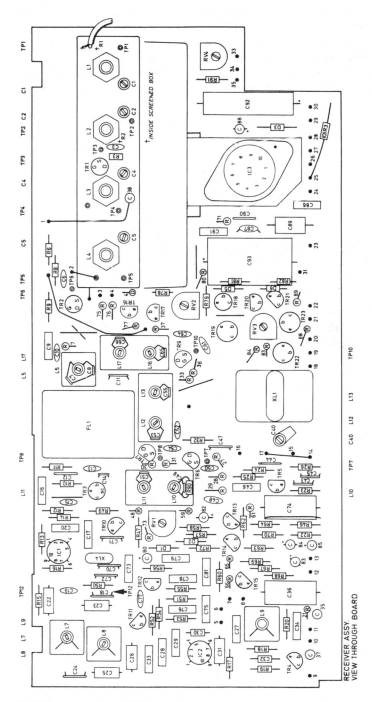

VHF Europa receiver PCB layout.

adjacent pin 1 on the PCB linking to the feedthrough capacitor on the front end block. Throughout the front end alignment, you'll need to be gradually reducing the actual level of the received signal as your receiver becomes more and more sensitive.

Tune the C5 adjuster, not necessarily with a non-metallic tool (you may need to use a pair of fine nosed pliers for instance), for best quieting of the received signal. Once you have done this, remove this DC link and instead link TP5 to chassis, and tune C4 for best quieting. Transfer the link now to connect TP1 to chassis, and tune C2 for best quieting. Transfer the link again now, connecting TP2 to chassis and tune C1 for best quieting, and then carefully re-tune L17 and L16 for best quieting using your ferrite adjuster for the latter two. Now remove the link, and give all four capacitors on the front end a final adjustment for absolute best sensitivity, i.e. maximum quieting of a weak received signal. Carefully re-tune the crystal trimmer if required for spot-on reception, and at this stage, if you have replaced the crystal filter, you may find that you'll need to slightly re-adjust L5 for minimum distortion of a modulated signal, otherwise leave it well alone.

Now onto the transmitter. Connect your power meter to the aerial connection, and key the TX on your crystalled channel, remembering to keep this keyed when taking readings. Connect your multimeter positive lead to TP1 on the transmitter board, keeping the range at 10 V DC. Initially tune C48 for maximum, then tune L3 for minimum. Transfer to TP2, and tune L4, then L3 for maximum, then L5 for minimum. Transfer the positive lead to TP3 and change the multimeter range to 2.5 V DC. Tune L6 and then L5 for maximum, then L7 for minimum. Transfer to TP4, tuning L8 and then L7 for

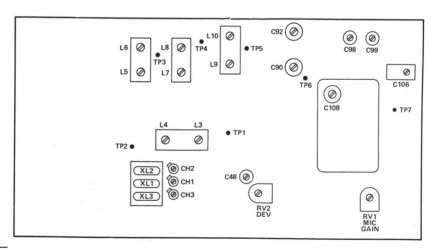

MF5FM transmitter alignment points.

maximum, then L9 for minimum. On to TP5 and tune L10 and then L9 both for maximum. Now remove the multimeter leads, and connect the positive lead to the DC positive supply, and the negative lead to TP6. Tune C90 and C92 using a flat-bladed non-metallic adjuster for maximum indicated voltage. Now remove the positive multimeter lead, change the range to 250 uA DC, and connect the negative lead to TP7. From now on, keep the TX keyed only for as long as it takes you to make an adjustment, to prevent overheating of the PA.

MF5FM Tune C98 and C99 for maximum indication on your multimeter, and you should now have an indication of RF power, so disconnect the multimeter and tune C106 and C108, the latter accessible from beneath the PCB, for maximum power. Re-tune the PA capacitors as required for absolute maximum, repeating several times as required.

MF25FM Tune C98 for maximum current indicated on the multimeter, then watching the RF power meter, tune C106, C107, C111 and C112 in that order for maximum RF output. Re-tune all the PA capacitors again for absolute maximum, repeating as required.

You may now find it useful to go through the multiplier and PA alignment stages again to squeeze the last drop of RF power out of the set. Set the relevant crystal trimmer for the correct transmit frequency, and while modulating the transmitter, adjust C48 as required for maximum deviation as copied on a monitoring receiver. RV1 which sets the mic gain will already be set fairly accurately, but RV2, the TX deviation control, may need slight adjustment to give

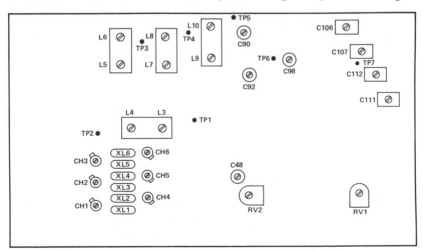

MF25FM transmitter alignment points.

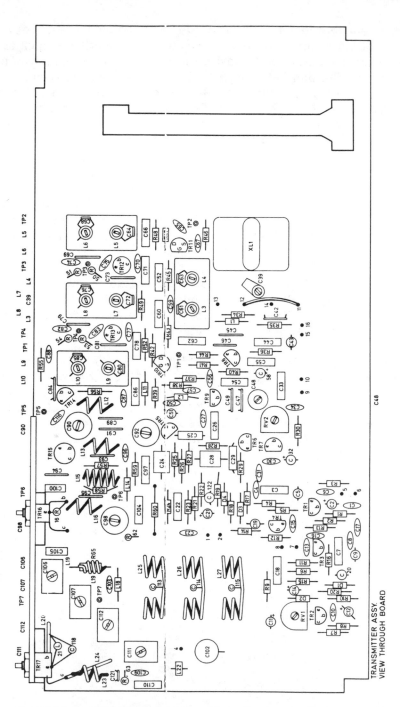

MF25FM transmitter PCB layout.

TRANSMITTER ASSY.
VIEW THROUGH BOARD

the required peak deviation. You may find that hinging the boards down often has a slight effect on the operating frequency of both TX and RX, so check this and re-adjust as necessary before finally screwing the case lids down.

UHF Alignment

As with the VHF set, we start by aligning the receiver multiplier stages. Switch to the appropriate crystal channel position, and connect your multimeter negative lead to the DC supply negative. Switch to the 2.5 V DC range and connect the positive multimeter lead to TP2. Using your non-metallic ferrite core adjuster tune L10 for minimum reading. Transfer the multimeter positive lead to TP3, and tune L11 and then L10 for maximum reading, re-adjusting as required for absolute maximum, then tune L12 for a minimum reading. Switch to the 10 V range on your multimeter, and transfer the positive lead to TP4. Tune L13, then L12, for maximum reading, again re-adjusting as required for maximum. Transfer to TP5, switch to the 2.5 V range, and tune L14 and L15 for maximum. Now switch back to the 10V range and transfer the lead to TP1. You'll now need to use a flat-bladed non-metallic trimmer to adjust the multi-turn capacitors C65 and C66, tuning these for maximum indicated voltage on TP1.

We now need to monitor an RF signal by using the aerial connector. Ensure the relevant crystal trimmer is adjusted so that you correctly receive a strong signal on the required channel. You may find it useful to open the receiver squelch at this point by adjusting RV1, the preset squelch potentiometer. On the metal front

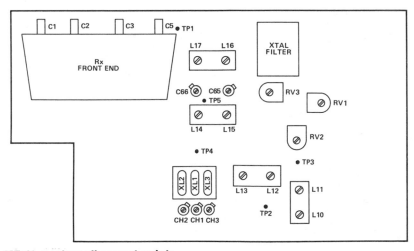

MF5U receiver alignment points.

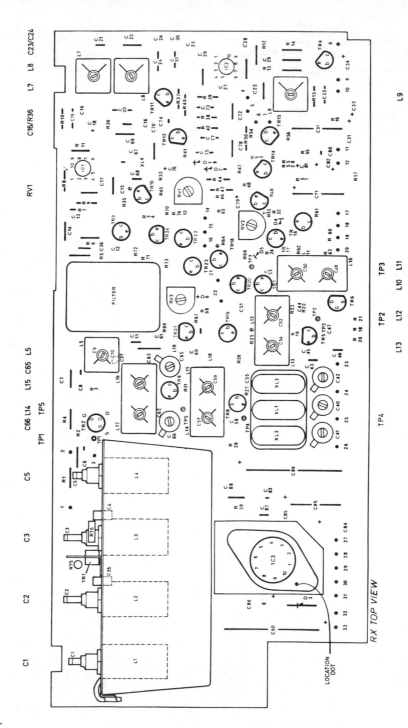

RX TOP VIEW

MF5U receiver PCB layout.

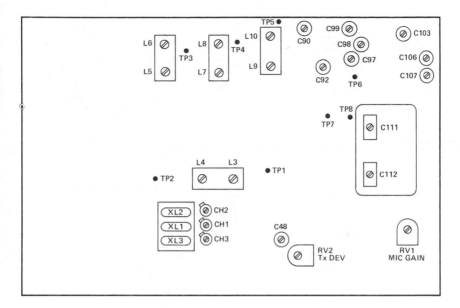

MF5U transmitter alignment points.

end block, adjust C5, C3, C2 and C1 for maximum quieting of a received signal, reducing the RF level of this as required. Again as with the VHF front end, you may find you need to use a pair of small pliers or suchlike for this if you don't have the correct tool; it is not necessary to use a non-metallic adjuster on these. Once you have done this, go back to C65 and C66 adjusting these for absolute best quieting of a weak signal, re-adjusting the trimmers on the front end block also for absolute best sensitivity.

Re-check the adjustment of each crystal trimmer for correct on-frequency reception, tuning these for minimum distortion of a modulated signal. Re-adjust the squelch as required, and that completes the receiver alignment.

To get the transmitter going, connect your power meter to the aerial connection, and with your multimeter switched to its 10 V DC range, connect its positive lead to TP1 on the transmitter PCB. Key the transmitter PTT, and remember to keep this keyed when taking readings. Using your ferrite core adjusting tool, tune L3 for a minimum voltage reading. Transfer the multimeter positive lead to TP2, and tune L4 then L3 for maximum reading, re-adjusting as required for absolute maximum, then tune L5 for minimum. Transfer to TP3 and switch your multimeter to its 2.5 V DC range. Tune L6 and then L5 for maximum reading, then tune L7 for minimum. Transfer to TP4 and tune L8 then L7 for maximum, then L9 for minimum. Transfer onto TP5 and tune L10 and then L9 for maximum.

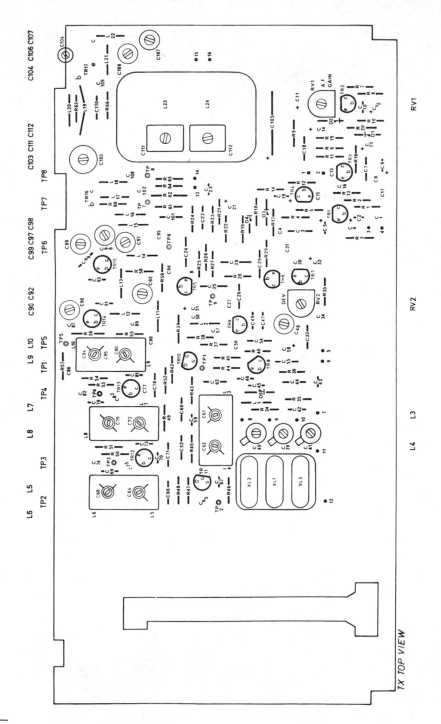

MF5U transmitter PCB layout.

Now remove the multimeter leads, and connect the positive lead to the + 10 V DC stabilised line present on pins 5 and 6 of the TX PCB, and the negative lead to TP6. Using your flat-bladed non-metallic trimming tool, adjust C90 and C92 for maximum reading. Now connect the multimeter positive lead to the 13.8 V DC positive supply, and the negative lead to TP7. Tune C97, C98 and C99 for maximum reading, re-adjusting again as required for absolute maximum. Transfer the multimeter negative lead to TP8, and tune C103 and C104, again for maximum reading. By now you should be getting an indication of RF power output, so try to keep the TX PTT keyed only for as long as you need for individual adjustments, to avoid overheating the PA. Tune C106 and C107 for maximum indicated power output, then tune C111 and C112 also for maximum output. Go back and re-tune these capacitors again for absolute maximum output, you may also find it useful to go through the DC alignment stages again to make sure you get optimum performance.

Adjust each crystal trimmer as required for the correct transmit frequency, and while monitoring on a receiver, adjust C41 for maximum deviation when modulating the transmitter, then adjust RV2 for the correct peak deviation as required. You'll find the TX microphone gain should already be set to a reasonable level, but this may be adjusted with RV1 to the required level.

Faultfinding

The most common fault you may encounter is that of no receive audio. First check that the audio link is in place between pins 8 and 12 on the facility socket, as a tone board that may have once been in place could have been removed for some purpose. If not fitted, a blank PCB with a connecting track linking these two connections should normally be in place, which of course may be missing.

If all is correct, check the squelch potentiometer – a spray of switch cleaner on this often works wonders, and try connecting an external 8 ohm speaker in case the internal one is faulty, remembering to keep the speaker leads isolated from the chassis. But if the large circular audio IC next to the front end block is getting hot, it is likely this has been destroyed, a very common reason for a set being sold as a 'scrap' bargain. This of course is of little consequence for packet radio use, but I would advise you to unsolder and remove the IC if it is overheating. If you do require loudspeaker level audio, I would recommend adding one of the many low-cost audio ICs, Maplin and Cirkit amongst others supply a variety of these. This may be built onto a small sub-board inside the set, fed from the wiper of the volume control. This carries fully squelched receive audio, and the output of the amplifier may of course be connected to the internal speaker as before.

The MF5AM Motafone

MF5AM Motafone

The Motafone is a compact, lightweight, self-contained 3 channel AM transceiver having its own built-in loudspeaker and wired-in microphone, the transmitter giving around 3 W output. This set is becoming available in abundance at very low cost, and I have rarely seen them sold at prices above a few pounds. As such, it could provide a very useful 'starter' for 4 m AM use on a channel such as 70.260 MHz.

All-In-One

The set comes as a simple-to-use unit, with just a volume control and a combined on/off/3-channel switch. Its small dimensions allow it to be placed in a variety of positions in a car's interior, alternatively it may happily sit in the 'shack', quietly awaiting calls from other 4 m AM users either on the normal calling frequency or your own 'net' channel. Low-cost original manufacturing techniques have been used on this transceiver, hence when choosing your set, a quick check around the case to ensure no physical damage has occurred would be worthwhile. A metal wrap-round cover is used, which may be slid off the set by removing the securing screws at the rear to enable you to take a quick look inside. I would recommend you reject any set that has been obviously damaged or subjected to many 'knocks', as the resultant intermittent faults could be rather difficult to resolve.

Preliminaries

Remove the wrap-round case as detailed, and check the two wire link fuses are in position on the small PCB fuse sub-board. These are 3 A fuses made up of 38 gauge tinned copper wire, and a pair of series chokes follow to reduce conducted ignition interference. If all is well, apply your 13.8 V DC power, and rotate the channel knob to the right from Chan 0 to Chan 1 to switch the set on, note these original markings are often worn as to make them illegible, so don't worry!

Turn the volume up to maximum, and rotate the RV2 preset potentiometer on the receiver PCB to defeat the squelch, you may not hear much squelch noise but you should hear a slight 'thump' from the speaker as the squelch opens. If not, check the heatsink next to the round audio IC, IC2, to see if it is getting rather hot with no audio output. This is a common cause of failure in the field, caused by shorting or grounding the loudspeaker leads. If you wish to connect an external loudspeaker to check, make sure that it has an impedance of greater than 8 ohms, the usual ex-PMR speakers being 3 ohms.

Crystals
The set uses HC25/u plug-in crystals, the commercial specification of these being T71 for both transmit and receive. The required frequencies for the 4 m band are:

$$\text{RX Xtal Freq} = \frac{(\text{RX Freq} - 10.7 \text{ MHz})}{2}$$

$$\text{TX Xtal Freq} = \frac{\text{TX Freq}}{2}$$

The Channel 1 RX crystal plugs into XL1 position, the Channel 1 TX crystal into XL4 position along the row of six crystal sockets.

RX Alignment
After you have plugged in your crystals, locate pin 13 on the crystal oscillator PCB, board 4, which is the local oscillator injection feed to the receiver from the crystal multiplier stages. We need to tune L8 and L9 on this PCB for maximum RF voltage on this point. If you have a diode probe, connect this to this pin and tune L8 and L9 with your ferrite trimming tool for maximum reading. If you don't have a probe and can't make one, you may be able to use a scanner receiver

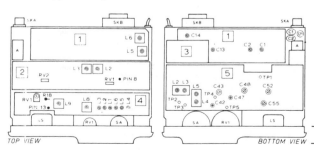

MF5AM alignment points.

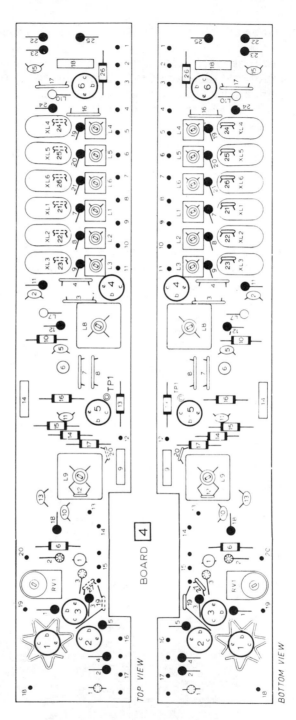

MF5AM crystal oscillator PCB layout.

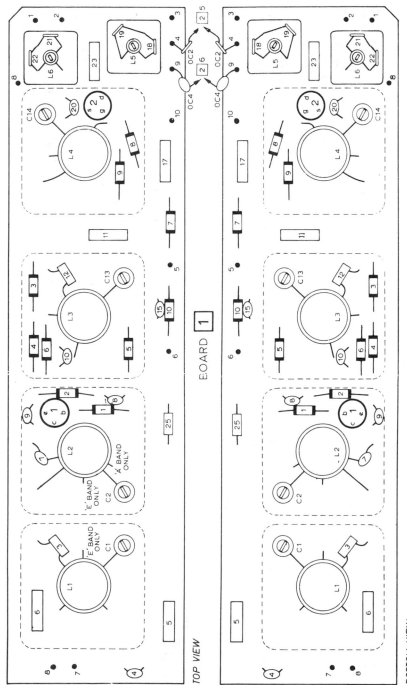

MF5AM receiver front end PCB layout.

or similar, tuned to twice the crystal frequency, using this adjacent to the Motafone to align for maximum radiated signal.

Now we need to receive an off-air signal at the wanted frequency (remember you can use your TX crystal in a simple one-transistor oscillator for this in the case of simplex frequencies), and initially tune L1, the crystal trimmer, for best signal to ensure you are at least near to the correct frequency. Now locate pin 8 on the receiver IF and Audio PCB (the one with the large single metal crystal filter), this is the receiver AGC line. Set your multimeter to its 2.5 V DC range, and connect the positive lead to pin 8, the negative lead to the DC supply negative. At this stage you may slightly re-tune L8 and L9 on the oscillator board for maximum sensitivity with a reasonably strong signal, indicated by maximum meter deflection.

Now while receiving a signal on the receiver front end board, tune L5 followed by the capacitors C14, C13, C2 and C1 on the large front-end coils, in that order, for maximum reading, keeping the RF signal strength at such a level as to keep the measured voltage around the 1.5 V mark. Re-tune these trimmers together with L8 and L9 on the oscillator board as required, again for maximum voltage, then as a final adjustment with a weak modulated signal tune C1 for the best signal-to-noise achievable. That completes the receiver alignment. Remember to re-set the squelch potentiometer RV2 as required, and to make sure your crystal trimmer is correctly adjusted for spot-on reception.

TX Alignment

Connect your RF power meter and load to the aerial connector, and locate the transmitter PCB, this is board 5 with the large metal NKT404 series modulator transistor fitted on its side. Set your multimeter range to 2.5 V DC, and connect its positive lead to TP3 on this board, with the negative lead to DC supply negative. With the microphone PTT pressed, tune L2 and L3 for maximum reading, re-adjusting as required for absolute maximum. Now transfer your multimeter positive lead to TP3 and adjust L4 and L5 both for maximum. Now disconnect your multimeter leads, and connect the negative lead to TP5 and the positive lead to the DC positive supply. Tune C42 and C3 together for maximum reading. You'll find it useful to use two trimming tools here, adjusting both capacitors in turn for absolute maximum. Transfer your multimeter negative lead to TP1 and tune C47 and C48 again for maximum.

By now you should be seeing some RF output power being indicated, so tune capacitors C52 and C55 for maximum power, followed by a re-tune of all the trimmer capacitors in the PA for absolute maximum RF power, and you should achieve at least 2.5 W carrier output. The TX modulation circuits do not require any

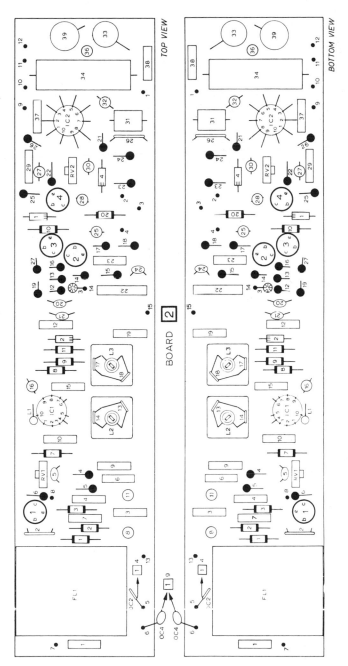

MF5AM receiver IF PCB layout.

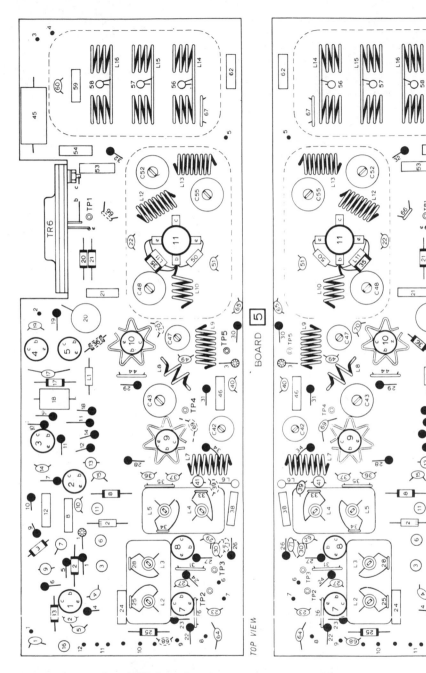

MF5AM transmitter PCB layout.

adjustment in terms of modulation gain or level, hence there is nothing to align here. All that now remains for you to do is to give the transmit crystal trimmer coil a tune to put you exactly on frequency.

Faultfinding
One of the most common faults found is that caused by physical damage, this may cause intermittent faults through cracked PCBs or broken solder joints on large components such as TR6 (the TX modulator transistor), or IC2 (the receiver audio amplifier). When removing the receiver IF and audio board, lift it vertically to avoid damage to IC2, this being inserted in a heat sink integral to the chassis. If you apply power to the set with this board removed, make sure some form of heat shunt is provided for IC2 to stop it overheating.

Other problems may be caused by the small loudspeaker being faulty and a quick check with an external speaker of 8–16 ohms impedance placed in parallel will confirm this. I have sometimes found the rear panel S0239 aerial connector to become corroded and hence a possible cause of transmit and receive problems. If in doubt clean this up or better still replace it if possible.

MF6AM Reporter

This set is becoming very popular now on the secondhand market due to its small size and high performance, and is in fact the type I have used myself for some time on 70.260 MHz. It is very suitable indeed for use on 4 m in areas where AM is used, its physical size being very small, similar to that of a standard car radio, and being AM it is, of course, often overlooked by many purchasers.

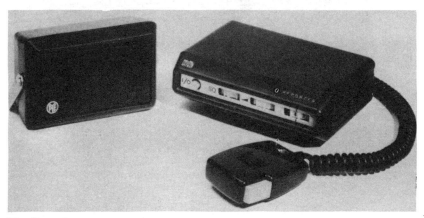

The Reporter.

Expect around 7 W transmitter power output, with good receive sensitivity limited mainly by external noise.

Identification and Selection

The rear panel will show the frequency band. Models were made to cover the following ranges:

E Band	68 – 88 MHz
P5 Band	79 – 88 MHz (TX)
P8 Band	96 – 106 MHz (RX)
M1 Band	105 – 108 MHz (TX)
M2 Band	138 – 141 MHz (RX)
A Band	148 – 174 MHz

The band to go for, of course, is E band for 4 m AM use. It is certainly not worthwhile to attempt to convert models to other bands, as this involves numerous coils and capacitor alterations. Note that for AM use it does not matter whether 12.5 kHz or 25 kHz filters are fitted apart from adjacent channel rejection requirements.

The single channel version is most commonly found, and a plug-in crystal oscillator board extends this to six channels where required, the multi-channel set being easily identified by the presence of a six-way channel switch. Some versions are found with external mic and speaker connectors, some with a wired-in speaker mic. The mic socket, if fitted, will be found on a flying lead coming from the rear panel, and the connections are the standard 5-pin DIN layout as for the Westminster, Europa etc. Likewise the speaker lead is the standard two-conductor affair, with brown and blue sleeved inner leads. You may find, apart from the normal red and black power leads, a pair of white leads emanating from the rear of the set. These are sometimes fitted and simply short together in combination with the set's power on/off switch to control external options, such as an A200 power amplifier.

Crystals

The crystals used are HC25u, the commercial specification being T71 for both transmitter and receiver. The frequencies given by the formula:

$$RX\ Xtal = \frac{RX\ Freq + 10.7\ MHz}{2}$$

$$TX\ Xtal = \frac{TX\ Freq}{2}$$

Internal view of the MF6AM

Preliminaries

The case is removed first by unscrewing the four M3 screws at the rear of the case, one in each corner, then sliding the entire case sleeve forwards. Note that it is not necessary to remove the plastic front panel. There are two printed circuit boards in the set, the uppermost is the 'LF' board containing audio and DC circuitry, the lower PCB is the 'RF' board containing the receiver RF and IF stages, crystal oscillators, and the transmitter multiplier and PA. To access the tuning components, remove the two screws securing the right hand side of the LF board, then loosen the single screw at the front of the LF board, securing this to the internal metal frame. The LF board may now be hinged upwards, a plastic bracket at the front holding it in this position.

Receiver Alignment

Plug your crystals into their appropriate sockets, and connect DC power and aerial coax connections. With your multimeter set to the 2.5 V DC range, connect the negative lead to the set chassis and the positive lead to TP1, (a small gold plated vertical pin). Using a small-

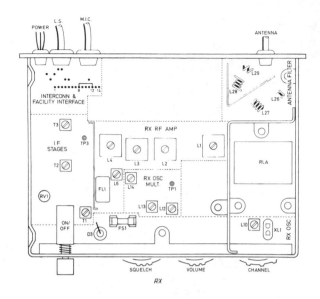

diameter ferrite adjusting tool, tune L12, L13, and L14 in that order for maximum reading, re-adjusting as required for absolute maximum. Now transfer the multimeter positive lead to TP3, and while receiving an off-air signal (adjusting the receive crystal trimmer first for best reception) tune L1, L2, L3, L4 and L6 in that order for maximum, keeping the level of signal down to achieve around 0.5 V at TP3 if possible. Finally re-tune these again for absolute maximum on a weak signal to ensure the best sensitivity.

You should not need to re-adjust any of the IF coils of course, as these will already be correctly aligned in a working set. However, you may find it useful to slightly re-adjust RV1, this is the IF gain setting potentiometer, to suit your operating needs. Note this will also shift the position of the squelch opening point, and with no aerial connected, all you will hear on no signal is a very slight 'thump' from the speaker at maximum volume when this occurs, so be warned! If you do find that you have no receive audio, and a 15 way D-type socket is fitted to the rear panel of the set, check that pins 8 and 7 are linked on this, alternatively that pins 8 and 12 are linked on the vertical pin array at the rear of the set main board which connects to this socket. These connections are used for external selective calling options, and the receive audio path is broken by these pins. You may have bought the surplus radio but not the accompanying tone unit.

Transmitter Alignment
Keeping the multimeter negative lead connected to the DC supply negative, connect the multimeter positive lead to TP2, and keeping

Reporter transmitter alignment points.

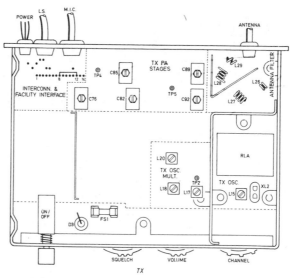

the PTT keyed, tune L17 for maximum, then L18 for minimum reading. Now use a diode probe if you have one connected to TP4 and tune L20 and C76 both for maximum, alternatively tune both these until you start to see a trace of RF power from the aerial connection. From now on, keep the transmitter keyed only for as long as you need to take a reading, to prevent the PA stages generating power when untuned. With a flat-bladed trimming tool, adjust C82 with C85, and C89 with C92, in pairs for maximum RF power output; a pair of trimming tools, one in each hand, is very useful here. Retune from L20 onwards as required for absolute maximum, and then finally adjust the crystal trimmer for the correct required frequency. The transmit modulation should be reasonably set already, however RV4 sets the peak modulation, RV3 setting the modulation gain. You may find you need to adjust these with the aid of off-air reports or by using test equipment, though in practice I would leave well alone.

Faultfinding

In the past, the problems I have come up against have been due to the on/off switch leads becoming intermittent or separated from their small gold-plated pins just beneath the on-off switch on the set. Check also the DC fuse, this is a 20 mm glass unit plugged into a PCB socket at the front of the RF board. If you find you have no audio, apart from the receiver links previously described, check the multi-way ribbon cable linking the two PCBs in case this has fractured at the narrow point where each track is soldered. The volume and/or squelch potentiometers sometimes go a little 'noisy' in use, and in some cases may result in no receive; a spray of switch

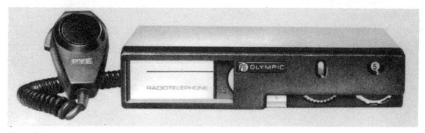

The Olympic.

cleaner onto their tracks will clear this up. If you have a crimped-on BNC connector on the aerial flying lead, check that the sleeve of this has not cut through the coax sleeve through excessive vibration in the past. This can cause lack of receive sensitivity and TX power problems.

OLYMPIC RANGE

The Olympic range is a series of dash-mounted mobiles, operating on VHF FM and AM and on UHF FM. Again, being a *range* they often look identical from the outside, but a look at the rear panel label will give a positive identification. They come in single, 6, and 12 channel versions allowing a good deal of flexibility.

On VHF FM, they give in the order of 17–18 W RF output, on 4 m AM around 8 W. UHF models give around 11–12 W. Being reasonably modern (as far as surplus equipment goes of course!) their receivers are quite sensitive, and there is seldom the need to make any improvements here. On transmit, the FM models use a 'block' PA module, hence no PA alignment is required. Even if you find an unrepairable fault on the receive side, it is certainly possible to remove the PA unit and use it separately as an add-on PA for a handportable for home or mobile use.

On the left hand side of the facia is a 'facility' slot to allow fitting of selective calling tone circuitry and the like. If your Olympic has a blank panel here, or indeed just an empty hole, don't worry, it will still work without it. If instead it has a sub-facia with an array of indicators and/or push buttons, then the module may easily be unplugged and the set instead linked internally for normal operation.

Identification
There are three basic versions of the Olympic:

M201 – VHF AM
M202 – VHF FM
M212 – UHF FM

They operate on one of the following frequency ranges:

M201
A Band: 148–174 MHz
E Band: 68– 88 MHz
C Band: 117–137 MHz
M1 Band: 105–108 MHz (TX)
M2 Band: 138–141 MHz (RX)
P8 Band: 96–106 MHz (RX) – combined with E band TX

M202
A Band: 148–174 MHz
B Band: 132–156 MHz
D Band: 88–108 MHz
E Band: 68–88 MHz

M212
T1-Band: 405–440 MHz
U0 Band: 440–470 MHz

You will see the manufactured equipment type and the band range engraved onto the rear metal label, this will be followed by the channel spacing of either S (12.5 kHz – M201/M202 only), R (20 kHz – M202/M212 only) or V (25 kHz – all models). You may also see the code 1, 6, or B signifying that the set is a single, 6, or 12 channel version. Ensure the frequency range will cover your needs, and likewise with the channel spacing. The 'A' band equipments will normally operate satisfactorily on 2 m, the 'E' band sets being ideal for 4 m of course; you will rarely find 'B' band equipments though. On UHF, 'U' band transmitters will normally tune perfectly but the 'U' band receivers will be at the extreme edge of their range on 70 cm and hence will sometimes only 'just' tune, but will still be adequately sensitive if a few dB 'down' on a 'T' band model. All UHF Olympics were built for 20 kHz or 25 kHz channel spacing, hence making them suitable for amateur use without crystal filter changes.

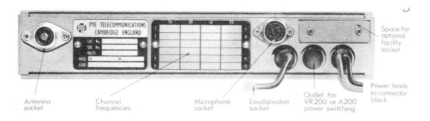

Antenna socket — Channel frequencies — Microphone socket — Loudspeaker socket — Outlet for VR200 or A200 power switching — Space for optional facility socket — Power leads to connector block

It's important to inspect the rear panel serial number plate to identify the set.

Beware of the 'P' band M201, which may often be advertised as a 4 m set but it will only operate there on transmit. You will find the receiver operates in Broadcast Band II and is rather difficult to modify, but it is far better to reject it or just buy it for the transmitter side, selecting instead a correct 'E' band M201 if you're after a 4 m AM set. Likewise don't be tempted to purchase an M201 hoping it is a simple matter to convert to FM. It isn't, and only a single conversion receiver is used, with an IF of 10.7 MHz, rather than a double conversion that could allow a 455 kHz discriminator to be added.

The sets are made using several plug-in 'daughter' boards assembled onto a main 'mother' board, with a die cast chassis used providing screening between them. You may also find additional tin-plate screens push-fitted on the top of the chassis between the circuit boards and the top lid. A useful check before purchase would be a quick look inside to ensure the crystal oscillator boards are fitted, and that no other PCBs are apparently missing.

Preliminaries

To remove the top lid, for inspection or alignment purposes, first push the latching On/Off switch upwards to the 'On' position. Then using a small pointed implement, press into the small hole at the right of the black front panel plastic facia, and at the same time hinge the facia panel forwards to allow its removal. You will now see the exposed 'control' board screwed to the front of the set, this may be left in place. Undo the two large screws at the front of the top lid, which can then be removed to expose the internal circuitry.

Be careful when unplugging the daughter boards, some are screwed to the chassis top (such as the RX audio board) and others have short coax links plugged in at the top (such as the FM TX driver). To prevent damaging the interconnections, remove the PCBs by pulling vertically rather than trying to lever them out at an angle. If a selective calling unit is present in the left hand side facility unit space, this may be safely removed by inserting the end of a small screwdriver into the hole on the lower front of the unit's facia, which unlocks the PCB, then withdraw the assembly out from the front of the transceiver.

If no selective calling facility board is present, check that pins 8 and 12 are linked on the 15 way PCB socket, pin 1 being at the extreme left with pin 15 on the extreme right. This is sometimes done using a PCB, having just a link track present, or sometimes with a wire link between two further PCB pins just behind this socket. This is the receiver audio link and must be in place for the receiver to function normally. If it is not there, for instance if a plug-in tone board was originally fitted, then make the appropriate link at the rear of the PCB with a short length of insulated wire.

Connections

The microphone connector is the standard 270 deg DIN type, with pin 1 as mic live, pin 2 screen, pin 4 carrying earphone audio and pins 3 and 5 as PTT, these switching the 10 V stabilised line. A suitable external speaker of 3-8 ohms impedance is required, connected at the rear of the set to the lead, having internal blue and brown insulated wires – don't confuse this with the adjacent DC power connections! On some sets you will find a thinner white insulated wire, used to control On/Off switching via an internal relay from the car's accessory supply. To switch the set on this lead must be connected to the supply positive. You may also find a 15-way D-type socket fitted, this being linked to the internal facility socket to allow external units to be connected.

M202 – VHF FM Crystals

The crystal formulae required for all bands in the M202 is:

$$ TX\ Xtal = \frac{TX\ Freq}{12} $$

$$ RX\ Xtal = \frac{RX\ Freq + 10.7\ MHz}{12} $$

The crystals are HC25/u type, the commercial specification of these is T54JO for all types. You should find some suppliers can offer ex-stock crystals for TX on popular channels, but you may have to order the RX types to be made to your requirements.

Alignment

Plug in your crystals, and select the channel, if appropriate, that is closest to the centre frequency of your TX/RX range. Rotate the volume control to around the mid-way position, connect your 13.8 V DC power supply and switch the set on by pressing upwards on the orange On/Off switch. Rotate the squelch control and check that you can hear the usual squelch noise, if not check the internal facility connector linking.

If you have purchased a set with the incorrect channel spacing, replacement of the 10.7 MHz crystal filter will often be sufficient to render suitable operation for amateur use, no matching components around this need changing (although the squelch will operate at a different threshold). The individual filters are identified by:

FC99001 12.5 kHz spacing
FC99002 25 kHz spacing
FC99003 20 kHz spacing (normally OK for 25 kHz amateur use)

Alternative crystal filters are available from suppliers listed in the Appendix.

RX Alignment

Set your multimeter to a low voltage DC range (1 V–2.5 V), with the negative lead connected to the DC supply negative. Adjust the Oscillator-Multiplier PCB (board 4) ferrite cores so that they protrude around 3 mm above the tops of their formers. Connect your multimeter positive lead to TP1 on the Osc-Mult board, and tune the cores of L3 and L4 downwards with your non-metallic trimming tool for maximum multimeter reading. As you tune, you will get *two* voltage peaks here, adjust for the *second* peak. Now transfer your multimeter positive lead to TP2, and likewise adjust L6 and L7 for the second voltage peak. Re-tune L3, L4, L6 and L7 slightly as required to achieve absolute maximum, you should get around 0.5 V. Now set the former of L9 so that it is flush with the top of the former before proceeding onto the front end. You may now disconnect the multimeter.

While receiving a reasonably strong signal on your crystalled alignment channel, initially adjust the appropriate crystal trimmer to bring the receiver onto frequency, i.e. tuning for best quieting followed by least distortion on a modulated signal. We now tune the receiver front end, (board 1) for best quieting from a signal received via the aerial connector. First tune C9 and C17 for best quieting, then C1, C5, C13 and C21 again for best quieting, reducing the received signal level as you progress. Now go back and tune C1, C5, C9, C13, C17, C21 and L7 in that order, again for best quieting of a weak signal, then slightly re-tune L9 on the Osc-Mult board as required for best sensitivity. Now re-check the crystal trimmer for spot-on reception, then adjust C25 on the front end board for best quieting. That completes the front end alignment.

The IF stages should already be aligned if the set came out of commercial use, however, if you have replaced the crystal filter it may be worthwhile to give T1 next to this filter a slight re-tune if required, adjusting this for maximum current (around 5 uA DC) on the adjacent TP1 on that board when receiving a signal on the correct frequency.

TX Alignment

Connect a suitable 50 ohm load to the aerial connector, and with

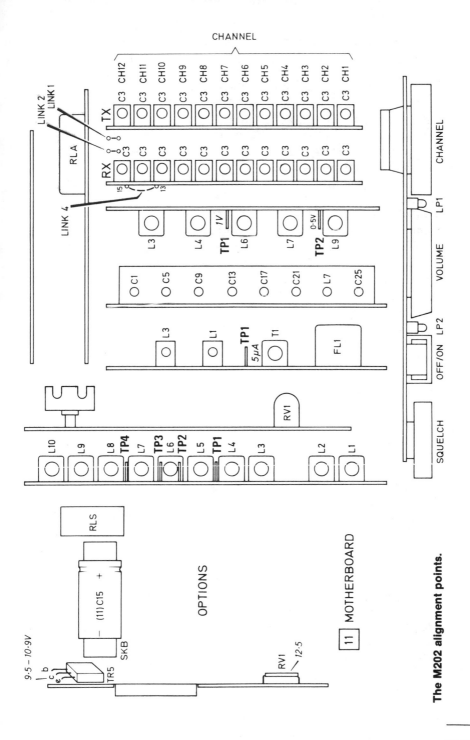

The M202 alignment points.

your multimeter switched to the 10 V DC range connect its negative lead to the DC supply negative, and the positive lead to TP1 on the TX multiplier board (board 8, just to the right of the facility housing). With the transmitter keyed, tune L1 and L2 with your non-metallic trimming tool for minimum multimeter reading, then tune L3 for maximum, you should get around 8 V at this stage. Transfer your multimeter positive lead to TP2 on this board, and tune L4, then L3 both for minimum, then L5 for maximum, you should get around 9 V. Transfer to TP3, and tune L6 and then L5 both for minimum, then L7 for maximum, you should get around 8 V. Now step your multimeter up one range, to indicate up to around 15 V, and transfer the multimeter positive lead to TP4. Tune L8 and then L7 both for minimum, then tune L9 for maximum.

You should by now be seeing some RF power from the transmitter, so tune L9 and L10 for maximum. If you don't have an RF power meter, you can place your meter set to the 10 A DC range in series with the positive DC supply lead to the transceiver, and tune these coils for maximum DC current drawn. Now adjust your crystal trimmers to achieve the correct transmit frequency, followed by adjustment of RV1 on the AF PCB for the correct peak deviation. Mic gain is pre-set and is not variable.

M212 – UHF FM Crystals
The crystals used are HC25/u size, the commercial specification being T64JO for both TX and RX. The crystal frequencies required for 70 cm are:

$$\text{TX Xtal Freq} = \frac{\text{TX Freq}}{27}$$

$$\text{RX Xtal Freq} = \frac{\text{RX Freq} + 21.4\,\text{MHz}}{27}$$

Alignment
After plugging in your crystals, switch the set on and check that, by rotating the squelch knob with the volume control suitably adjusted, you can hear squelch noise from the speaker. Connect your multimeter negative lead to the DC supply negative, and select the crystalled channel nearest to the centre of your crystalled frequency range, if appropriate.

RX Alignment
On the Oscillator-Multiplier PCB (board 4) adjust the ferrite cores so they protrude around 3 mm above the tops of their formers. Switch

your multimeter to the 2.5 V DC range, connect the negative meter lead to DC supply negative and the positive lead to TP1 on the Osc-Mult board, and tune C3 on this board for maximum reading. Transfer to TP2, and with your ferrite core trimming tool, tune L2 and L3 for maximum reading, choosing the tuning point with the core at its inner position. Transfer to TP3, and tune L4 and L5 for maximum, again choosing the tuning point with the core at its inner position. Transfer to TP4, and do likewise with L6, tuning for maximum. Keeping your meter lead connected to TP4, slightly re-tune C3, L2, L3, L4, L5 and L6 as required for absolute maximum, then adjust C22 at the end of the PCB for minimum reading.

Now connect the meter positive lead to the set chassis, and the negative lead to TP1 on the front end PCB (board 1), with the meter set to its lowest DC voltage range. Using your non-metallic trimming tool tune the cores of L9 and L10 for maximum reading, and slightly re-adjust C22 as required for absolute maximum, you should get around 0.2 V.

If aligning a 'U' band set, I would recommend initially tuning the remaining front end coil adjusters so that they are almost at their lowest positions, corresponding to maximum inductance, making subsequent adjustment easier. If tuning a T band set, leave them at their original positions. While receiving your off-air signal, adjust the relevant crystal trimmer to place the receiver onto the correct frequency. Now tune L2, L3, L4, L5, L6, L7 and L8 in that order for best signal, reducing the signal level as required for tuning purposes. Re-tune for absolute best quieting on a weak signal, then re-tune L9 and L10 slightly as required. Re-check the crystal trimmer adjustment to ensure spot-on reception, repeating on each crystalled channel if appropriate, and that completes the receiver alignment.

TX Alignment

Connect your 50 ohm load to the aerial connector, and your multimeter negative lead to the DC supply negative. You will need to remove the lower case lid here, as some of the multiplier tuning points are only accessible through holes from beneath the motherboard. Switch to the 10 V DC range on the meter, and connect the positive lead to TP1 on board 8, this is the TX multiplier board just to the right of the facility module housing.

With the transmitter keyed, tune L1 and L2 on this board with your ferrite core adjustment tool for maximum voltage reading. Transfer to TP2, and tune L4 for maximum, accessed from the lower side of the motherboard, then re-adjust L1 and L2 again slightly for maximum. Transfer to TP3, and tune L6 and L7 for maximum (L7 from the underside), re-adjusting L4 slightly for absolute maximum

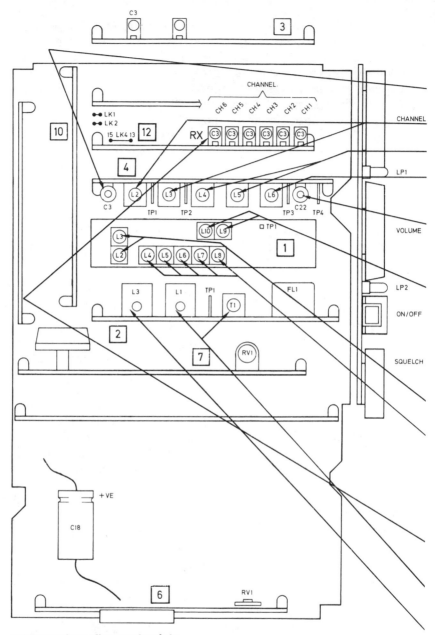

M212 receiver alignment points.

again. Transfer to TP4, and tune L8 and L9 for maximum, then go back and slightly re-adjust all previous coils as required for absolute maximum on TP4.

If aligning a 'U' band set, I would recommend placing the cores of

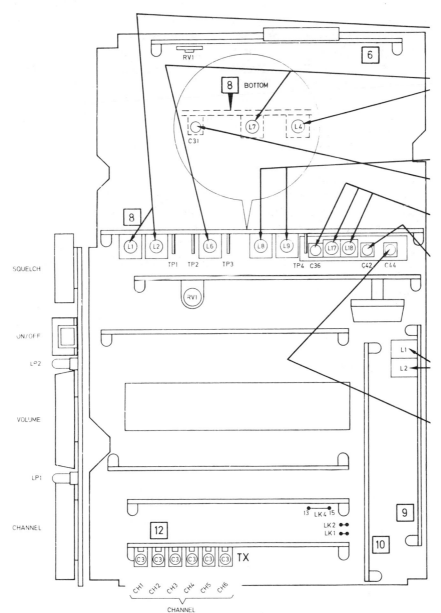

M212 transmitter alignment points.

L17 and L18 to be almost bottom of their travel, otherwise with a 'T' band set leave them in their original positions. We now need to use a diode probe, connected to the metal adjustment slot of C36. Tune C31, accessible from beneath the motherboard, for maximum reading. Transfer the diode probe now to the metal adjustment slot of C42, and tune C36, L17 and L18 in that order for maximum reading. L17 and L18 comprise a band pass filter, and the correct adjustment point will result in these being in approximately the same positions in their formers. Now connect your diode probe to the adjustment slot of C44 and tune C42 for maximum reading. Keeping your diode probe on this point, slightly re-tune C31, C36, L17, L18, and C42 as required for absolute maximum reading. If you don't have a diode probe and cannot make a simple one, then you could place an ammeter in the positive DC supply line, and attempt, by trial and error to tune until you see a slight rise in the current drawn, then having started, continue for maximum current.

Now keeping an eye on the RF power meter, tune L1 and L2 on the rear panel mounted PA board for maximum RF power, re-tuning C44 for absolute maximum. Finally, adjust each crystal trimmer as required to place you on the correct frequency, and set the transmit peak deviation using RV1 on the audio board alongside the TX driver board. Note this is a peak deviation adjustment only, the mic gain being pre-set.

M201 – VHF AM
This set is available very cheaply on the surplus market, and as with other E band AM sets, it can provide an economic 4 m transceiver in areas where AM is used.

Crystals
The crystal frequencies required for 4 m are given by:

$$\text{TX Xtal Freq} = \frac{\text{TX Freq}}{2}$$

$$\text{RX Xtal Freq} = \frac{\text{RX Freq} + 10.7\,\text{MHz}}{2}$$

The crystals used are HC25/u can size, the commercial specifications of these being T71 for both TX and RX. Note these frequencies are common to those used in other 4 m AM sets, so crystals may be exchanged between equipments if required in the future, the crystals normally costing more than the equipment in practice.

Alignment
Plug your crystals into their respective sockets, ensuring you get them in the correct places. XL1–12 are receiver channels 1–12, XL13–24 are transmitter channels 1–12, on both 6 and 12 channel versions. On single channel sets, XL1 is the receive crystal with XL2

the transmit crystal position. Check that the receive audio link as previously detailed is in place. You will need to remove both upper and lower case lids, as the tuning adjustments on the receiver front end are only accessible from beneath the motherboard. Connect your speaker and 13.8 V DC supply. Switch the set on, select the appropriate channel, and rotate the volume and squelch controls fully anti-clockwise initially.

RX Alignment

Adjust the cores of board 5 (the RX multiplier) to be flush with the tops of their formers, and those of board 1 (the front end) accessible from beneath the motherboard, to be 3 mm above the tops of their formers. Switch your multimeter to a low DC voltage range, and connect the negative lead to the DC supply negative. Connect the positive lead to TP1 on board 5, the receiver multiplier, and with your ferrite trimming tool tune the appropriate crystal trimmer (L1 for channel 1) initially for maximum reading, you should get around 0.3 V indicated. Now transfer to TP2 on this board, and adjust the core of L1 downwards until a maximum multimeter reading is achieved, then tune L2 downwards for minimum. You may find if you continue tuning, a further peak or dip is achieved, but it is the first tuning point we need to use here. Now transfer to TP3, and tune the core of L3 downwards for maximum, again taking the first tuning point, then tune L8 for minimum. Keeping your multimeter positive lead connected to TP3, slightly re-adjust the cores of L1, L2 and L3 for absolute maximum.

Now connect your meter positive lead to TP1 on board 2, the IF Amp/Detector/AGC board. With a received signal on your crystalled channel, first turn up the receiver volume and adjust the crystal trimmer for the correct reception frequency by tuning for the best signal. Now tune the front end board coils L1, L2, L3, L4, L5, L6, L7 and L8 in that order, adjusting from beneath the motherboard for maximum reading on TP1, reducing the received signal level at each stage if possible to keep the measured DC voltage around the 0.5 V mark. A final re-tune of these to get absolute best reception followed by a check of the crystal frequencies completes the receiver alignment.

If the set came out of service, the IF stages should be adjusted correctly, so do not touch these. If however, it has suffered the fate of the 'adjust everything' merchants then the following steps would be worthwhile. T1 on module 2 must be adjusted for maximum reading on TP1 when receiving a signal, using the second tuning point when adjusting the core downwards from being flush with the top of the former. When receiving a moderately weak signal (0.4 uV pd to be exact), turn the squelch control fully anti-clockwise, and

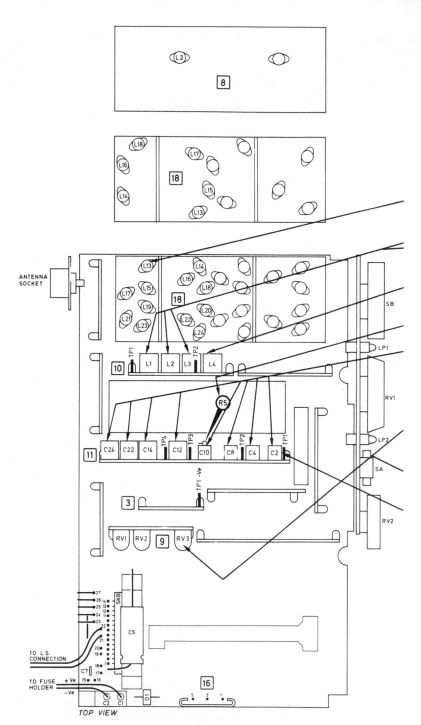

M201 receiver alignment points.

adjust RV1 for a DC voltage of 1.0 V on TP1. Then transferring to TP1 on board 7 (the board just behind the on/off switch) keeping the received signal coming in, tune the core of L2 on board 6 for minimum reading, this time selecting the first tuning point when tuning downwards from the core being flush with the top of the former.

TX Alignment

First of all, adjust all the TX multiplier PCB (board 10) ferrite cores to be flush with the tops of their formers. For the initial stages of alignment, remove the PA unit (board 11) and place a 47 ohm resistor across the motherboard pins 1 and 3 previously occupied by the PA (you will see a suitable test resistor, R5, placed on motherboard 'parking' pins for this purpose). Alternatively, connect a suitable 50 ohm load to this point, preferably with some form of sensitive RF power detection.

Select the 250 uA range on your multimeter, and connect the negative lead to supply negative, the positive lead to TP1 on the multiplier PCB, board 10. With the transmitter keyed, tune the appropriate crystal trimmer coil (L2 single channel, L13 multi-channel for channel 1) for maximum indicated current, this will be around 35 uA. Now remove the multimeter positive lead, change the range to 2.5 V, and connect to TP2. Tune L1 for maximum, then L2 for minimum, then L3 for maximum on the test point.

We now need to tune for maximum RF output into the resistor R5, either by using a diode probe here or some other form of sensitive RF power detector, even an adjacent receiver could be used. Tune L4 for maximum RF, then re-tune L1, L2, L3 and L4 again for absolute maximum. Now you can remove the DC power, replace R5 back to its 'parking' pins or otherwise disconnect your 50 ohm load from pins 1 and 3, and replace the TX PA assembly. Connect your 50 ohm load to the aerial connector, and switch the set back on.

Set your multimeter to the 10 V DC range, and connect the positive lead to TP1 on the PA assembly. Adjust RV3 on board 9 (the potentiometer towards the front of the set) for a measured voltage of 5.0 V on this test pin. From now on, you will find the use of two tuning adjusting tools useful, one in each hand, but note these adjusters *must* be non-metallic otherwise you risk destroying the PA transistors. Remember to keep the transmitter keyed for only as long as is necessary to obtain a reading, to save the PA transistors operating in a mismatched state for long periods. Place a diode probe on TP2 of the PA, and tune C2 and C4 together for maximum, then transfer the probe to TP3 and tune C8 and C10 together for maximum. Transfer to TP4, and tune C12 and C14 together again for maximum, by now you should be seeing some RF power indicated

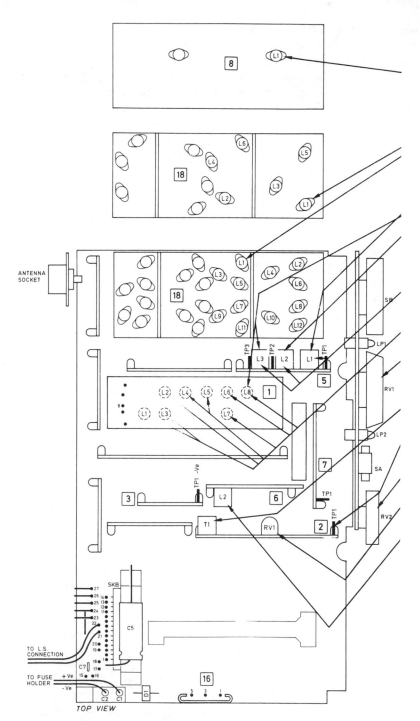

M201 transmitter alignment points.

from the aerial socket. Tune the output capacitors C22 and C24 together for maximum RF, then re-tune the previous capacitors again in pairs for absolute maximum, you should achieve around 16 W on 4 m.

We now need to go back to RV3 on board 9, and re-adjust this to obtain 8.0 W of RF power, to ensure the PA will be operating in its linear portion under modulation conditions. Finally re-adjust your crystal trimmer coils as required to obtain the correct transmit frequency. The modulation stages should already be adjusted correctly if the set came out of service, but if these require altering board 9 RV1 sets the microphone gain, and RV2 sets the modulation depth. The depth should not exceed around 90% on any channel to prevent overmodulation and hence splatter.

Faultfinding – Olympic Series
The majority of faults I have come across have been due to 'dirty' contacts between the motherboard pins and the mating sockets on the plug-in modules. Dust may enter the case and can sometimes cause intermittent connections here, as can exposure to humid conditions in a corrosive atmosphere. As a matter of routine, I would wholehearted recommend you to remove the boards, which can unplug without unscrewing or unbolting operations, and quickly clean the pins and sockets with a suitable spray cleaner. Do *not* however, use an abrasive cleaner, and *never* be tempted to use sandpaper or a small file on these pins, this will certainly cause problems in the months to come!

Another fault sometimes occurs on UHF transmit, where the small coax link between the driver and PA stages becomes broken at the outer, often caused by vibration, and a quick soldering job here affords a cure. If you find no transmit power at all on the M202/M212, check for drive power at the input to the PA; replacement of the module is an easy matter. These modules have been individually sold on the surplus market at prices of less than £10 in the past, but check that the cost of these does not exceed that of another Olympic in the first place.

If you find no crystal oscillation occurs on the M202/M212, check that in the oscillator compartment the links marked 2 and 4 are fitted in the case of single channel sets, or that links 2 and 4 are removed but link 1 is fitted in the case of a single channel set. These allow either sets of oscillator PCBs to be fitted, which may have been changed or removed prior to finding their way onto the market.

Modifications
On FM Olympics, the transmitter power may be varied by altering the voltage to pin 5 of the UHF PA module, or pin 3 of the VHF PA

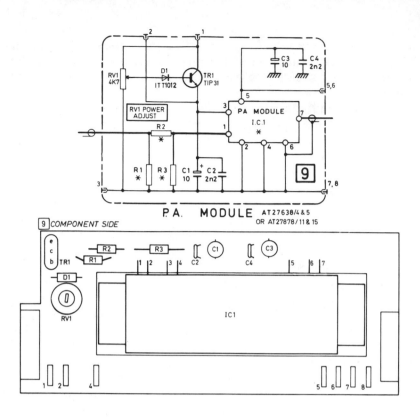

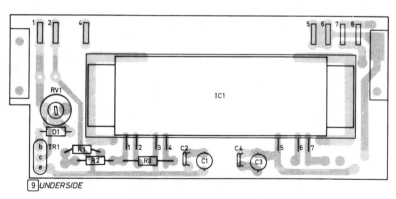

Variable transmitter power modification for the M202.

module (note this is the module pin, not the PCB pin). This is normally linked to the PCB sockets to connect to the motherboard, but you will find room on the PA PCB for a potentiometer and series pass transistor to be fitted if required. A 4k7 potentiometer between the supply rails with the slider used to vary the base voltage on a PNP transistor such as a TIP31 will allow variable power. Alternatively a simple switch used to link a series wirewound resistor in and out of circuit to this pin will provide a low/high transmit power facility. Of course there is ample room on the unused facility panel for such controls.

If you wish to use the facility unit space to house a toneburst, you will find that socket pin 3 is connected to the microphone audio input, pin 1 being ground, pin 7 carries switched 10 V on TX, pin 9 carries 12.5 V, and pin 11 carries constant regulated 10 V.

For packet radio interconnection, pin 2 on this socket is a 'busy' lamp control, and may be used via a resistor to control the base of an NPN switching transistor for squelch detection, this point being 0.5 V squelched, 1.5 V unsquelched. Pins 8 and 12 are of course linked and carry the receive audio.

A200 Linear Amplifier

The A200 is a 'stick it in the boot and forget it' add-on linear amplifier. Not many amateurs realise that PMR equipment of days gone by could sometimes do with a few extra watts when trying to achieve the maximum in range. Improvements in base station receivers, coupled with the ever increasing need for spectrum re-usage, has meant that these units are increasingly finding their way onto the amateur market. Inside these sturdy weatherproof boxes you will find a piece of mint-looking board with a 50 W – plus linear amplifier, complete with automatic RF sensing and change-over switching. Just the job for 2 m, 4 m, or with some modifications, 6 m.

The A200

Identification

The A200 is easily identified as a solid die-cast unit with heat dissipation fins on its topside, and are always painted black. It always has three connections at the end, these being RF input, output, and a thick DC power lead. The only similar looking unit around has the same outer case but with two thick d.c. leads coming out of the side, this is a type VR200 24 V to 12 V converter, so don't be misled by appearances.

There have been two types of A200 in manufacture, an early model having a TNC RF input socket and an N-Type RF output socket, and you may sometimes find a later model, with one SO239 output socket and a flying coax lead for the RF input. Internally they are virtually the same, but you may find the later model arrangement is easier to install. The DC cable is actually a very heavy current AC cable, with brown, blue, and green/yellow leads – brown is used as the positive 13.8 V supply, blue as negative, and green/yellow as a switching lead, but please don't wire it up to your mains plug as the capacitors inside make a lovely exploding noise!

Selection

On the side of the case, you will find a riveted plate with "Cat No. A200" marked, and below this is space for the aligned frequency of operation. Unfortunately this is often blank, but take a look at the section marked "Code", you will see something like "01 E0", which provides the frequency band information. The first two numbers are the market code which is irrelevant for our purposes, the final

A200 identification from the serial number plate.

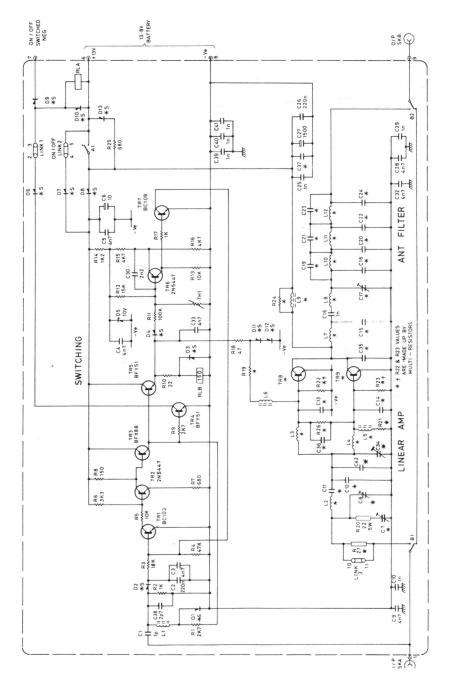

A200 circuit diagram.

letter/number combination gives the frequency range:

E0: 68–88 MHz,
M1: 105–108 MHz,
B0: 132–156 MHz, and
A0: 148–174 MHz.

The E0 is useful for 4 m, and both the B0 and A0 models will tune to 2 m. The E0 model will also, with the modifications described, operate very satisfactorily on the 6 m band.

Circuitry

Internally, a pair of MPX085P or BLW60 transistors are used, which have forward bias applied via a wirewound resistor and two forward biased diodes. Input and output printed circuit inductors together with compression trimmers and a three stage low pass filter are used in the RF path, a further capacitor and plate resistor on the input form a gain control to ensure the amplifier is operating in the linear portion of its input/output curve. RF sensing circuitry detects input drive, and switches in the amplifier if DC power is supplied. The unit is extremely rugged both physically and electrically, and even incorporates an over-temperature cutout to stop the transistors overheating in use. I have never yet seen a faulty amplifier sold, but it would be wise to check inside to ensure there are no components that have obviously been removed.

Preliminaries

Check that the internal pins are correctly linked, with pins 2 and 3 connected together, and pins 4 and 5 connected together. This will ensure that the RF sensing circuits will always be powered up, ready to switch DC to the amplifier itself via the internal DC relay when RF is detected. If you wish to use a small toggle switch for on/off switching however, make sure both of these links are removed and then use a switch between the green/yellow DC wire and 0V to connect the amplifier into circuit. When not switched in, RF input and outputs are simply linked for a 'straight through' connection.

Connect up your DC supply, with positive to the brown wire, negative to the blue wire on the thick power lead, ensuring your power supply has the current capability required. As a guide, a 10–15 A 13.8 V supply will be required for maximum output with a 10 W nominal drive power. Connect up your transceiver to the RF input connection, and a suitable load capable of handling 60–70 W to the RF output. If your A200 has a TNC input connector, you may find it more useful in practice, to remove this and replace it with a coax lead, terminated in a PL259 or BNC as appropriate to suit your transceiver.

A200 internal view.

Tuning

Alignment to 2 m or 4 m is extremely simple. Initially set C7 for minimum capacitance, i.e. its vanes fully apart. This is used as an 'RF Gain' adjuster, to reduce the input drive power to the amplifier stages. Whilst transmitting 2 W–15 W of RF power into the unit, check that the relays click over, and simply tune C8 and C17, both for maximum power output, re-tuning as required until you cannot achieve any further increase. If you have an in-line SWR meter, you may like to insert this in the coax between your transceiver and the A200 amplifier, and re-adjust C8 slightly as required for minimum indicated SWR, this should coincide with maximum RF power output.

You will typically get around 50–60 W output for 10–15 W input, with less than this of course with reduced input drive. If you intend using the amplifier on AM (see later for SSB), then it is important now to adjust C7 until you reduce the output power to around 25 W. This will ensure the amplifier will handle the positive peaks of modulation presented to it from your transmitter.

SSB Modifications

As the A200 is a linear amplifier, it will of course handle SSB quite well. However, as it was originally designed for remotely mounted AM/FM use, as soon as the RF power falls below a given level the amplifier relays cut out, and as a result, use on SSB causes a good deal of relay 'chattering' and broken transmissions. We may add a

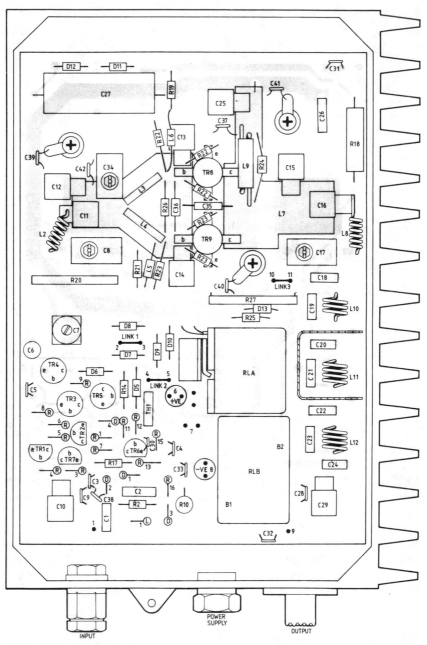

A200 component layout.

suitable 'hang time', i.e. a switch-off delay, by adding a small electrolytic capacitor across C2 and C3. A value of 0.68 uF will give around three-quarters of a second delay which I have found is the

Leabharlanna Ceantrach Atha Cliath

most acceptable, 0.47 uF gives around a half second, and 1 uF around one second. Any capacitor of at least 10 V working voltage will suffice. Fit the capacitor with its positive lead to the D2 cathode/R3/C2/C3 junction and with its negative lead to the PCB ground plane.

You may also find it useful to increase the RF switching sensitivity, to prevent losing the first syllable of speech following a pause in transmission. To do this, fit a small ceramic capacitor of around 4.7 pF in parallel with C1 on the A200, this will increase the RF detection sensitivity to below 50 mW. Both of these additional capacitors may easily be soldered to the component side of the PCB, hence removing the need to extract the main board from the chassis.

Following this, tune the amplifier as described with C7 at minimum capacity. Once this has been done, adjust C7 so that the output RF power *decreases* by approximately 10%, this will ensure you are not overdriving the amplifier and that it is operating in the linear portion of its transfer characteristic. After doing this, you may find that you need to slightly readjust C8 for optimum output power. As a guide, you will typically achieve around 45–50 W PEP power output with 28 dB rel. PEP level 3rd order IMD products. Don't try to squeeze the last drop of power out on SSB, this will degrade the linearity of your signal, resulting in audio distortion and splattering across a wide bandwidth.

6 m Conversion
In view of the cost of commercial amplifiers for the 6 m band, it is certainly a worthwhile exercise to modify an A200 from E0 band to the 6 m band. The requirements in this respect are good linearity and a very well suppressed level of 2nd harmonic output, this falling in the UK Broadcast Band II and hence being rather undesirable! The following is a result of theoretical calculations and initially several practical modifications done by myself, together with many dozens more, following a published article by myself on this.

Low Pass Filter Modification
The low pass filter is made up in three sections and employs accurately made coils and tubular capacitors of close tolerance. It was decided to retain the original coils and only to modify capacitor values to save any coil rewinding efforts. The existing filter was designed to pass 68–88 MHz whilst attenuating the harmonics of these, which means that it offers little rejection of 100 MHz, a check on a Network Analyser confirmed this to be the case. So please *do not* attempt to use an E0 A200 by simply modifying the amplifier, ensure the low pass filter is modified as a priority. You may certainly

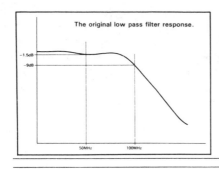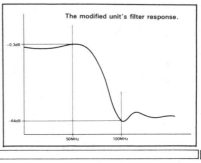

A200 Low-pass filter response.

achieve a good RF output but the second harmonic rejection of the LPF will be less than 10 dB which will make you very unpopular.

The accompanying table gives the modifications required in capacitor values, although please *don't* be tempted to use 'near' values for the low pass filter section dependant upon what your junkbox holds. Use close tolerance silver mica or ceramic plate capacitors of the exact value, unless of course you use tubular ceramics as originally fitted. Note that some capacitors require changing, whereas others require an extra capacitor added across the original one.

You will need to remove the internal board to carry out the changes. When removing the three central screws securing the main heatsink block to the chassis, take care not to break the 1nF decoupling capacitors fitted on the solder tags. You will also need to disconnect the RF input and output leads, but the board may still be hinged out if you leave the d.c. power wiring connected. Watch out for the heatsink compound smeared on the underside as it is terrible stuff to get off your clothes. After the low pass filter capacitor changes, all further work may be performed from the component side of the board so you may safely do the screws back up to keep the compound away from fingers etc.

Amplifier Modifications

Again, existing inductors may be retained, and additional capacitors simply added where required. This time, most types of capacitors may be used, values not being too critical, but ensure you use the shortest lead lengths possible. This is particularly true in the case of the added capacitors across C12, I found several in parallel to be the best. If you are feeling extravagant, Cirkit supply Semco mica-wrapped capacitors which are ideal for this use, and you will see this type of capacitor already used on the input and output stages.

Across C12 you may see a silver mica 180p capacitor added, which was sometimes used on manufacture when the amplifier was

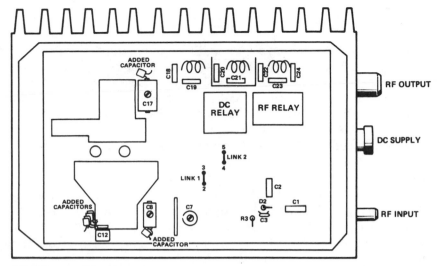

A200 6m modification.

tuned below 78 MHz. On late models with a flying input lead, as opposed to input chassis-mounted socket, you will see a variable capacitance trimmer of 30–140 pF. You will need a total of around 750 pF extra; if the 180 pF capacitor is fitted then subtract that, and if the trimmer is fitted, set that to maximum (adjuster screwed tight) and subtract 140 pF. Four 180 p capacitors in total are ideal, soldered between the board earth plane and the input matching network board as shown. The two other capacitors required are soldered between the side connections of the trimmers as shown, and the board earth plane. Make sure you use a hot soldering iron to avoid dry joints here.

Following these modifications, tune the amplifier as previously described. If you wish to use it on SSB then the switching modifications may also be carried out. On 6 m, you will typically get around 50 W PEP output, with a 2nd harmonic level of less than −80 dBc.

A200 Component Modifications – 6 m
C8 Add 120 pF in parallel with existing trimmer
C12 Add 750 pF in parallel (see text)
C17 Add 68 pF in parallel
C18 Replace with 56 pF
C19 Replace with 39 pF
C20 Add 68 pF in parallel
C21 Replace with 18 pF
C22 Add 68 pF in parallel
C23 Replace with 5.6 pF
C24 Add 39 pF in parallel

THE WHITEHALL

The Pye Whitehall is an AM *and* FM mobile transceiver, being capable of either mode of operation on a channel-by-channel basis. A wide bandwidth on both transmit and receive is accomplished through the use of pre-set varicap tuned stages, these transceivers being made with government users in mind. On the surplus market, there have been several types, some of which operate on M band (100 MHz) receive which are hence of little use unless extensively modified. Others however, originate from ex-RAF usage and are capable of operating on the 68–88 MHz range on both transmit and receive, and these are ideal for 4 m. Another excellent factor here is that if you travel or even live between areas where occasionally AM is used on 70.260 MHz, and others where sometimes FM is found on 70.260 MHz or 70.450 MHz, your single transceiver will suffice nicely.

A 20 W output power level is provided on transmit, with an adequate receiver sensitivity for normal 4 m use (although DX-chasers may wish to add a simple BF981 preamp). Up to 10 crystalled channels may be fitted, each may be individually linked for either AM or FM transmit or receive, or with a simple modification, independent AM/FM switching may be provided from the control box.

A transmission timer is employed in the unit, this limits the maximum TX period to approximately 30 seconds to prevent the accidental interference when used in normal service. This facility of course may not be advantageous for amateur use, and it may easily be defeated if required.

The Whitehall.

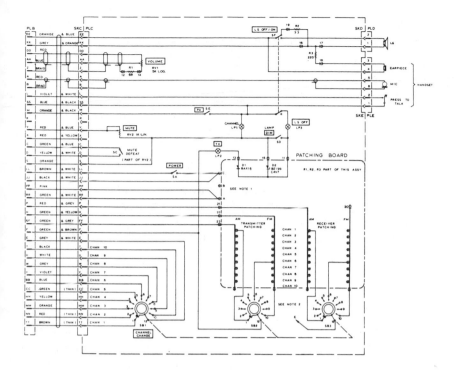

Whitehall control unit circuit arrangement.

Identification

The Whitehall has the model number W20AM/FM, which is normally engraved on the equipment serial number plate. Be careful to check that the frequency coverage of the equipment, as marked, is for transmission *and* reception in the 68–88 MHz range. Reject any other, as due to the very low cost of suitable surplus gear of this vintage (1971), in my opinion it simply isn't worthwhile attempting to perform extensive modifications.

As all Whitehalls are remote mount equipments, make sure also that you obtain the matching control box if these are offered for sale. If not then the accompanying diagrams show the connections required if you feel it worthwhile to make your own unit. Note the wiring of the handset connections for microphone audio and transmit switching, these differing to the rest of the 'usual' surplus gear on the market, hence you will probably have to manufacture a suitable lead, unless of course you were fortunate in acquiring the matching telephone handset as well when purchasing the transceiver.

Crystals

The required crystal formulae for use on 4 m with a 68–88 MHz set are:

$$\text{TX XTAL FREQ} = \frac{\text{TX FREQ}}{12}$$

$$\text{RX XTAL FREQ} = \frac{(\text{RX FREQ} - 10.7\,\text{MHz})}{2}$$

Both crystals are HC6/u size, the transmit crystal being operated in fundamental mode with 30 pF series capacitance nominal, the receiver crystal being 3rd overtone resonant, these being the parameters you may need to state when ordering suitable types for 4 m use.

Preliminaries

The top and bottom panels are released by giving each one of the quick-release fasteners on each lid corner a twist. You will also need to slide off the perforated shutter on the front panel to access the multiple potentiometers which set the required varicap bias voltage for each channel. Open the set up, and plug in your appropriate crystals. To set the required mode for each channel you will also need to open up the control unit by unscrewing the two 4BA size socket head bolts on the control unit front panel. Inside you will find four lines of 10 pins each, arranged in a matrix. These are marked with RX AM and FM, also TX AM and FM, the numbers 1–10 corresponding to the channel numbers. You will need to fit (or alter the positions of existing) patch leads here as indicated in the control unit circuit diagram, arranged as required to provide the mode/channel arrangement you wish to use. Note that the controller push button marked 'LS' switches the external speaker in and out of circuit, receive audio only being heard in the telephone handset earpiece in this case, so make sure you have the speaker enabled when aligning the set. Note that the 'LS' light is normally lit when the speaker is disabled as a 'warning'. A 'Public Address' facility is switched in by the 'PA' button, in this case high level amplified microphone audio is supplied to drive an external 15 ohm horn speaker.

Varicaps

On the varicap bias control board, you will find the following potentiometers control the bias voltage applied to the TX/RX stages:

POT.	TX Chan.	POT.	RX Chan.
RV1	1	RV2	1
RV3	2	RV4	2
RV5	3	RV6	3
RV7	4	RV8	4
RV9	5	RV10	5
RV11	6	RV12	6
RV13	7	RV14	7
RV15	8	RV16	8
RV17	9	RV18	9
RV19	10	RV20	10

Pin 10 on this PCB feeds the pre-set voltage to the RX stages, pin 11 feeds the TX stages. As the 4 m amateur band is essentially narrow in bandwidth, I would recommend setting the relative output voltage to a nominal but identical value, e.g. 7.00 V for each channel *before* any RF alignment is attempted.

Receiver Alignment

After setting the varicap supply voltage, set your multimeter to the 2.5 V DC range and connect its positive lead to TP1 on board 5, the RX multiplier PCB, with the negative lead connected to your DC supply negative. Using your non-metallic trimming tool, adjust the core of L1 on this board for maximum indicated voltage, then tune L3 for minimum. Now remove the positive multimeter lead, switch to the 50 uA current scale, and transfer to TP2. Tune L4, L3, and then L1, in that order, for maximum reading, retuning as required for absolute maximum, this completes the multiplier alignment.

Now onto the front end: you'll need to receive an off-air or locally generated signal now on your crystalled receive frequency. Initially tune your crystal trimmer inductor to ensure on-frequency reception on your selected channel. On PCB No. 1, the RX front end, tune T1 for best reception, i.e. maximum audio of a weak AM signal or best quieting of a weak FM signal. If you have the channel in use linked for AM, you may now wish to connect your multimeter set to the 50 uA DC current range to TP3 on PCB No. 3 (the 455 kHz AM IF), and tune all front end stages for maximum indicated current when receiving a signal. Alternatively, even if you wish to receive FM, you may care to temporarily link the channel in use for alignment to AM to enable you to use this tuning level indication. After tuning T1, adjust L4, T2, L3, T1, L2 and L1 in that order for best reception, repeating as required for absolute maximum on a weak signal. As a final measure, you may fine-tune these for best audible reception on a weak signal, i.e. maximum audio on AM or best quieting on FM.

Now re-check your crystal trimmer adjustment to ensure spot-on

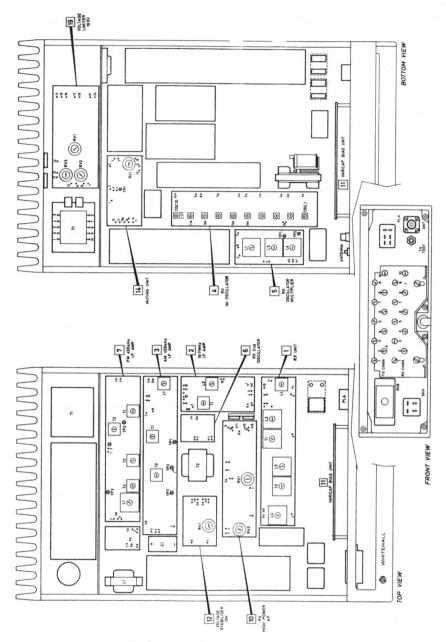

Whitehall receiver alignment points.

reception, repeating on each channel in turn. You should not normally find it necessary to readjust the varicap bias voltages on other crystal channels if operating within the confines of the AM/FM sections of 4 m. However if one or more of your crystalled receive channels are far removed in frequency from your alignment channel, you may now slightly readjust the relevant varicap bias potentiometer for best sensitivity on these channels, otherwise I would advise you to leave these adjustments well alone.

Transmitter Alignment

After plugging in your crystals and selecting the appropriate mode links in the control unit, and pre-adjusting the varicap bias voltages as described, switch your multimeter to the 10 V DC range and connect the positive lead to TP1 on PCB No. 21, the wideband TX modulator and multiplier board, with the negative lead to the DC supply negative. With the transmitter PTT keyed, adjust the cores of L3, L4 and L5 on this board for maximum reading. Note that you'll need to watch carefully here for a very slight rise initially, if you have difficulty you may place a diode probe on pin 7 on this board and adjust L3 and L4 for maximum, then tuning L5 for maximum DC voltage on TP1. Readjust these again for absolute maximum indicated voltage on TP1. Now transfer your multimeter positive lead to TP2 and L7 and then L6 for maximum, re-tuning as required for absolute maximum. Transfer to TP3 and tune L9 and then L8 both for maximum, again retuning as required. Remove your multimeter positive lead, change the range to 50 uA DC and connect to TP4. Tune L11 and then L10 for maximum, making sure you achieve at least 20 uA on each crystalled channel, if not, repeat the alignment procedure. If insufficient current is being indicated on a crystalled channel far removed in frequency from your alignment frequency, you may now try slightly readjusting the relevant TX varicap bias potentiometer for maximum.

Now on PCB No. 22, the Wideband Driver board, unsolder the coax inner from pin 5 and in its place connect a coax link, inner to pin 5 and outer to pin 4, feeding a sensitive RF power meter such as a milliwattmeter or a quarter/half watt carbon resistor with a diode probe coupled to it. With the transmitter keyed, tune the cores of L4 and L5 on this board for maximum indicated power, you should achieve at least 250 mW here. Now re-connect the coax link, and we can proceed onto the Power Amplifier alignment. Remember to keep the transmitter keyed only as long as is necessary to take a reading from now on, to prevent the PA transistors from operating into a mismatched load for long periods.

With your RF power meter connected to the aerial socket and a suitable 50 ohm load attached, key the transmitter and tune C1 and C2 together for maximum indicated voltage on TP1 on this board, you should at this stage start to see RF power indicated. You'll find the use of two trimming tools, one in each hand, useful here. Now

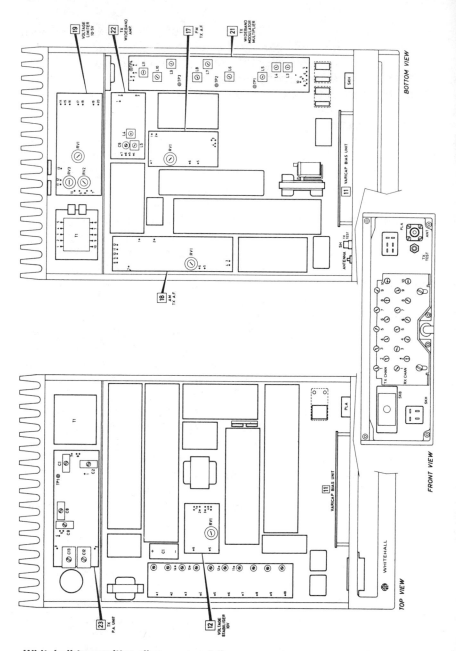

Whitehall transmitter alignment points.

adjust C12 and C13 to maximum capacity, i.e. vanes fully meshed together, and adjust C8 and C9 together, and then C12 and C13 again together for maximum indicated RF power. Readjust these capacitor pairs as required to give absolute maximum, you should find you achieve at least 20 W RF power output.

For AM use, the transmitter modulator stages will already have been set to around the correct levels if the set came out of active use, however if this needs adjusting then RV1 on the AM TX audio board, PCB No. 19, should be set to give 67% modulation with normal microphone level audio, with RV3 set to provide a peak modulation level of 80% under heavy modulation conditions (i.e. a loud shout into the mic). On FM, RV1 on PCB No. 17, the FM Transmitter Audio board, sets the peak deviation, the mic gain being at a fixed level.

Modifications

As we have seen, the Whitehall is a versatile transceiver for 4 m AM and FM operation. One very useful modification however, is that of external AM/FM switching facilities on the control box, to allow, for instance, AM or FM use on frequencies such as 70.260 MHz without the need to duplicate crystals. This may be done in one of two ways:

1) By using alternate channels or 'banks' of channels designated for AM and FM use. This is done by simple internal links to the channel switch lines feeding the crystal oscillator lines (*not* the AM/FM patch lines), i.e. linking pin TT for channel 1, pin NN for channel 2 etc. This method is best described by example. Let's take the case of using channel 1 on 70.260 MHz AM, and channel 2 on 70.260 MHz FM. After suitable patch links being fitted as appropriate for the required modes on these channels, simply link the crystal switching lines 1 and 2, i.e. pins TT and NN, together with a wire link. With your crystals placed in either the channel 1 *or* channel 2 positions, you will now gain operation on this frequency on both channels but with alternative AM and FM modes.
2) If you prefer a dedicated AM/FM switch, you may use one of the unwanted change-over switches on the controller, i.e. 'PA', 'DIM' or 'LS' for this purpose. Here instead of linking the patch leads to the required AM or FM lines for transmit and receive, link the 'common' line of these, i.e. the appropriate channel switch rotor connection, to the dual-pole change-over switch common pin. Then link the other pins to the required AM and FM switching lines, to provide an AM/FM function independent of the channel selected. Remember to link the original switch wire connections together as required, to resume the original operation function.

Transmit Timer Modification

As many amateur QSOs have longer 'overs' than the 30 seconds allowed by the internal TX timer, this facility may be removed if required. The timer circuitry resides on PCB No. 16, a small board with four connections at the end. A pair of capacitors, C1 and C2 of 22 uF each wired in parallel are slowly charged through a resistor R1 when transmit voltage is applied. To defeat the timer, simply remove R1 by cutting one of the leads, alternatively fit a shorting link across one of the capacitors. If you wish to run a 'hands free' mobile mic you may care to experiment by increasing the resistance value of R1, or adding further capacitance (e.g. 100 uf) in parallel with C1 and C2, either of these actions will extend the time period allowed, to prevent you accidentally leaving your TX switched on.

5   PORTABLE EQUIPMENT

THE PF1 POCKETFONE

In the 1960s, life changed dramatically for the policeman on the beat in Britain, with the introduction of the first ever truly portable radio equipment available, the Pye PF1 TX/RX, quite a revolution in its time. The receiver is normally carried in a top pocket, and has its own small internal aerial. The separate transmitter is carried in a side pocket and taken out when required. A novel feature of this unit is that on depression of the PTT button, a six inch quarter wave aerial rod pops up giving better performance for a low power set than an internal aerial. I remember with amusement being at a football match in my younger days, watching a constable extracting the aerial which unfortunately went right up his nose on transmit!

Insides

The receiver is a double conversion superheterodyne, with IFs of 10.7 MHz followed by 100 kHz. A battery economiser is used which effectively switches the receiver on for around 60 mS every 600 mS, thus prolonging battery life. When the squelch opens, this is

The PF1s.

Late model PF1
receiver with
speaker (left).
Early model PF1
receiver with
transducer (right).

defeated of course, staying in the 'open' state for two seconds after the squelch has closed to allow for signal fades in any blind spots of the coverage area. If you place a working receiver to your ear, you may hear a soft 'pulsing' noise showing the economiser to be in operation and the battery to be OK.

An internal plate aerial is used on early sets, together with a small transducer acting as a speaker beneath the aerial. This gave a characteristically 'tinny' audio reproduction, but later receivers employed a miniature speaker which improved on this, where the speaker frame doubled as the aerial. Examination of the case front will show an extension in depth at the top to house the speaker on the later equipments. The typical sensitivity achieved is around 1 uV p.d. for 12 dB SINAD, although this may easily be improved as will be seen later.

The transmitter utilises a standard oscillator, phase modulator, and multiplier approach, giving typically 100 mW into its quarter wave aerial. Although this is relatively low power in comparison to other sets, it is often perfectly adequate when communicating with a base station or repeater, and matches the receiver performance nicely.

Batteries

A 9 V nicad battery is used to power the receiver, this being the same size as the common PP3 but with different connections at the top. If you can't get hold of the correct nicad then a standard PP3 battery clip may easily be fitted and this used instead. An 18 V nicad battery is used in the transmitter unit, of the same depth and width as the receiver battery but twice the length. Again if you can't get hold of the correct batteries, two PP3s fitted end to end and connected in series will do nicely.

Both receiver and transmitter batteries are rated at 80 mAh, in use they will give around 10–20 hours of normal operation in both units. There are three connection points at the top, the centre is always positive and the two outer connections are both negative, and these are internally linked. To recharge the batteries, use a current limited supply at 8 mA, charging for 14 hours from a completely flat state. A standard PP3 battery charger circuit is ideal for the receive battery for instance.

Full Duplex Operation

A useful feature when operating with these sets through a repeater is the ability to get 'listen through' on your signals. This means that you can hear your own signals coming back as you talk, and can instantly tell whether you have whistled the correct tone to bring the repeater up, or whether you are 'doubling' with a stronger station or whatever. Also when used when communicating with a base station using different frequencies for TX and RX you can have a full duplex conversation; it certainly has interesting possibilities!

The PF1 pair allow full duplex operation.

Channel Spacings

The equipments were manufactured for both 50 kHz and 25 kHz channel spacing. This means that the receiver may have either a +/-15 kHz or a +/-7 5 kHz filter fitted, and the accompanying transmitter will similarly be preset to either 15 kHz or 5 kHz peak deviation. The transmitter may be modified simply by changing one resistor value, but receiver modification involves the change of a crystal filter. Unless you expect to receive reasonable strength signals at +/-25 kHz spacing, for instance a local repeater on the next channel, you probably won't have any problems. However by opening up the receiver case you may discriminate between the two by the markings on the large metal crystal filter:

FILTER TYPE FC03219 : 25 kHz SPACING
FILTER TYPE FC03208 : 50 kHz SPACING

If you do have problems, surplus dealers are known to stock replacements, although it would be best to check inside the receiver before purchase if you live in a congested 70 cm area.

Crystals

The crystals are both HC18u wire ended, the frequencies required being:

$$\text{TX XTAL FREQ (MHz)} = \frac{\text{TRANSMIT FREQ (MHz)}}{36}$$

$$\text{RX XTAL FREQ (MHz)} = \frac{\text{RECEIVE FREQ (MHz)} + 10.7}{5}$$

In the commercial band of 450–470 MHz, subtractive rather than additive mixing is used in the receiver, which means that the image frequency will fall in the 70 cms band. This can certainly be a great advantage, as if you have a choice of receivers, then take a look at the rear serial number plate and note the frequency marked on it, if shown. Note that some receivers do not have this shown for security measures. If you find one marked exactly 21.4 MHz higher than your intended receive frequency then a quick retune is all you need, no crystal to buy! For instance a receiver on 454.750 MHz will be fitted with the correct crystal to operate on 70 cm channel RB14, 433.350 MHz. Many suppliers do not remove the crystals as this entails removing a screening can and its associated tiny fixings as well as desoldering the crystal itself, this being rather more difficult than the usual exercise of unplugging a visible crystal.

Choose the right PF1 and you may not even need a new receiver crystal.

Transmitter Alignment

Remove the case back and desolder the main board output link from the aerial connection. You can now gently hinge the transmitter out from its case. In place of the aerial, connect a piece of coax, inner to the link tapping point and braid to earth, leading to a 50 ohm load (a 47 ohm 1/4 watt resistor serves well) via a power meter or some form of power indication such as a diode probe or absorption wavemeter. Remove the transmitter PCB screen by undoing the small nuts on the track side of the PCB and desolder the existing crystal, replacing it with your own, keeping lead lengths short. Replace the screen carefully before alignment, as its proximity will affect tuning.

Set your multimeter to a low voltage range, ideally 1V maximum deflection, and connect the negative lead to supply negative. With an 18 V supply, either from the battery or an external power supply, key the transmitter and tune the core of L1 for maximum voltage on the TR6 emitter test point. Note that this will be fairly broad, with a typical reading of 0.25 V; don't worry if a definite peak cannot be achieved initially. Then transfer your multimeter positive lead to T7 emitter, tuning L2 and L3 for maximum, typical reading 0.4 V. Transfer to TR8 emitter, tuning L4 and L5 for maximum, typical reading 0.7 V. Now set your multimeter to the next voltage range up,

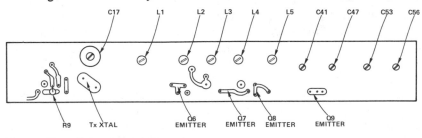

Transmitter alignment points.

around 2.5 V ideally, and now use a flat bladed non-metallic trimming tool to tune the variable capacitors at the end of the board.

Adjust C41 for maximum voltage on TR9 emitter, finally retuning slightly the previously adjusted coils for absolute maximum voltage at TR9 emitter, typically 1.8 V. Now place your multimeter, set to a current range around 100 mA, in series with the 18 V supply. Set C53 and C56 for minimum capacity, i.e. vanes fully apart, and tune C47 for maximum current indicated on your meter. By now you should be seeing some output power on your in-line power meter or diode probe, so set C56 for maximum capacity, i.e. vanes fully meshed, and tune C53 for maximum power output, then retune C56 again for maximum. Carefully re-adjust C47, C53, and C56 for absolute maximum output, you should be able to get around 100 mW of RF power. The internal aerial may now be reconnected, and then if you wish, slightly readjust C53 and C56 for maximum radiated power if you have access to a field strength meter, although in tests I have only achieved a very marginal improvement by doing this.

Final frequency setting is performed by adjusting C17, accessible through a hole in the screen. We now go back to L1 which is the phase modulator coil, by an on-air check on an adjacent receiver, tune L1 for absolute maximum transmitted audio level.

If you find audio level reports on 70 cm are reasonable, then I would leave the deviation setting alone, as it will already be set to near 5 kHz. However, if every speech peak drops you out of the squelch then it probably appears you have a 15 kHz deviation set and by altering the value of R9, a set resistor value, you may vary the peak deviation to the required amount. I would suggest a miniature 1 Meg potentiometer placed in line, at least temporarily until the required level is found, then replacement by a fixed resistor of the nearest value can be made. The telescopic aerial originally had a small plastic disc fitted to the top, but these invariably get lost in commercial usage. To avoid facial damage in use I would advise you to add a similar form of protection to the top.

Receiver Alignment

Remove the case back and hinge the receiver board out carefully, sliding the earphone socket out first. Remove the large silver-plated metal screen by undoing the four tiny securing nuts, two on the PCB side and two on the top of the screen. Underneath this you will find the receiver crystal, desolder this and replace it with your 70 cm crystal, then replace the screen, remembering to tighten the nuts carefully. The positioning of this screen is critical to the tuning, so if you remove it for any reason again you will need to retune the receiver to obtain the best possible performance. You will also see a

further crystal outside the can, this is the 10.80 MHz conversion

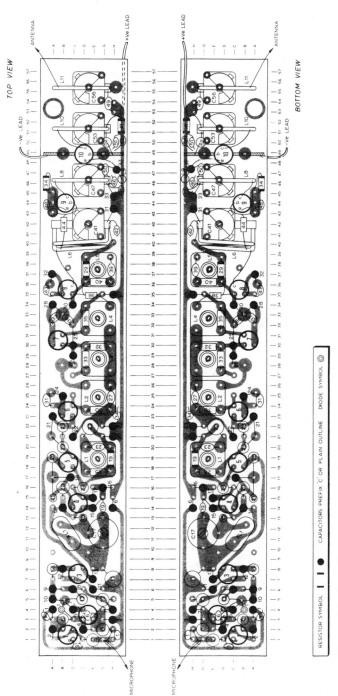

TOP VIEW

BOTTOM VIEW

RESISTOR SYMBOL ▮ ▮ ●   CAPACITORS PREFIX 'C' OR PLAIN OUTLINE   DIODE SYMBOL ⊛

Transmitter layout.

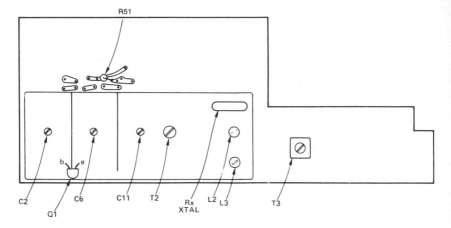

Receiver alignment points.

crystal which should be left in place.

Before applying power, temporarily short out R51 to defeat the squelch, this will considerably aid tuning. Connect a 9 V supply, either from the battery or an external voltage source, and check you hear squelch noise from the speaker or transducer. If not, then examine the contacts on the earphone socket, this is often a cause of problems when the mating connection in series with the audio output becomes corroded slightly. Using your ferrite core trimming tool, tune L2 for least distortion of a received signal with modulation present, to initially net the receiver onto frequency.

By reducing the input signal level until a detectable amount of noise is present, tune T2 and L3 alternately for the best quieting, reducing the received signal level further, as required. Now tune C2, C6, C11, and C18, again for best quieting, with a flat-bladed trimming tool. Note that these adjustments will be fairly sharp, particularly C6 and C11, so take care. If you intend using the internal aerial, carry out the final tuning of C2 with that aerial connected and the receiver mounted as far as possible in its plastic case to ensure the best performance. Once you cannot get any better quieting level on a weak signal, you can try slightly retuning L2 again for absolute best (least distorted) reception, and then remove the link from R51 to return the squelch to normal operation.

Note that some 'alignment instructions' photocopied and produced in an authentic looking light blue cover are commonly sold at rallies, often alongside PF1s for sale. They instruct you to leave L3 alone and tune T3, this is incorrect. T3 should not need realignment as it is the 10.7 MHz I.F. coil, and if you don't tune L3 you'll have a deaf receiver.

Inside the PF1s,
transmitter (left)
and receiver (right).

PF1 Receiver Improvements

If you find the receiver weak-signal performance lacking when portable you may like to try fitting a six-inch quarter wave aerial made from a piece of stiff wire in place of the internal aerial, though watch your eyes, place some form of protection at the end. A small coax socket fitted to the case top will allow you to plug a whip or helical in when portable (see the 'Accessories' chapter for a low cost high performance helical design), or allow the use of an external aerial from the home QTH.

Alternatively, an improvement in overall sensitivity of between 3 dB and 6 dB is achieved by replacing the RF amplifier transistor TR1, mounted inside the receiver front end screen between C2 and C6, with a BFY90, available from several component dealers. The base connects to the C2 side original connection point, the collector to the C6 side original connection point, and both emitter and screen are soldered to the internal dividing screen. Ensure you keep the transistor leads short. No further component changes are required, but you will find that you will need to retune the receiver front end stages slightly after fitting. I have performed this modification to several sets in the past with good results each time.

THE POCKETPHONE 70 RANGE

The Pocketphone 70 series is currently the most commonly

Three different Pocketphone 70s, the PF2UB (left), PF2UH (centre), and PF5UH (right).

available type of portable transceiver on the surplus market, both from specialist dealers and in the large number seen in the second-hand columns of amateur radio magazines and packet radio bulletin boards. It is however just what it says, a RANGE. There is absolutely *no* outside difference, besides the rear label, between a 78 MHz AM rig and a 432 MHz FM rig in the range. Your friend may think he recognises one by sight at a rally, and may unwittingly recommend one to you for purchase because it 'looks like' the one he's got. Also beware of the advert or description of a rig as a 'PF70'. Although this is sometimes used as a 'collective' phrase, if someone describes a rig he's selling to you solely as a PF70 then beware – he doesn't have a clue what he's talking about. So many people have unfortunately been misled in the past here, often due to ignorance on both sides, don't be one of them! If you're looking for a rig suitable for the amateur bands, then examination of the rear label will reveal an equipment type number:

PF2FMB Three channel VHF FM bodyworn, with external speaker/microphone. **PF2FMH** Three channel VHF FM handheld, with internal speaker/microphone. **PF3FMH** Similar to PF2FMH but with higher TX output power. **PF2AMB** Three channel VHF AM bodyworn, with external speaker/microphone (fairly rare, this one). **PF2UB** Three channel UHF FM bodyworn rig, with external speaker/microphone. **PF2UH** Three channel UHF FM handheld rig, with internal speaker/microphone. **PF5UH** Single channel UHF FM handheld rig, with internal speaker/microphone and internal aerial.

Sometimes the equipment type number will be followed by '2e', for example 'PF5UH2e'. This is a special, intrinsically safe equipment designed for use in hazardous areas such as oil rigs, where sparks or whatever could not be very welcome! Of course, if you work in a petrol station.... The PCBs of these are coated with a rubbery 'gunge' which is extremely difficult to remove for fault finding, the sets give lower TX output power, and (theoretically) need special tools to remove batteries and so on. This can often make their second-hand value a little less. There are currently a far greater number of UHF equipments available than VHF, but when selecting a VHF set, ensure you obtain a set of the correct channel spacing, i.e. 12.5 kHz or 25 kHz according to your needs. The PF2AMB manufactured on frequency bands suitable for retuning for amateur use is fairly rare, and hence is not covered here.

Sub-Tone
If you see a low audio frequency marked on the 'Code' section of the rear label, i.e. CODE 94.8 Hz, this shows that the set has at one time been fitted with a sub-audible tone lock circuit. The resonant reed plug-in modules are often removed prior to sale, making the sets incapable of correct operation, surplus plug-ins being very rare. It is possible to remove this circuit and fit required links to enable normal operation, which requires removal of the main board from the case, but it is much easier to choose a different set from the inevitable pile on the rally stand.

Bodyworn
The bodyworn versions are handy to stick in your pocket or fix onto your belt, with the speaker/mike clipped to your lapel. A matching leather case often comes included in the price with the set, which can be very handy. The bodyworn facility saves your top pocket being weighed down but still enables you to hear a call without deafening everyone around you. The aerial socket here is a miniature type TNC, sometimes difficult and expensive to get plugs for, so make sure you obtain a matching aerial or change the socket

Bodyworn unit.

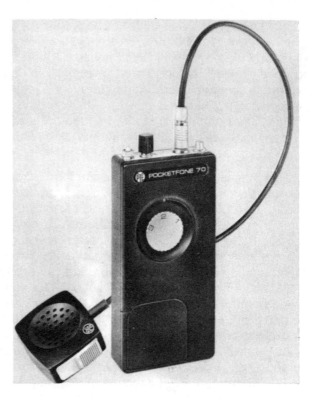

PF2 bodyworn microphone connections.

1 – EARTH
2 – SPEAKER/MIKE
3 – PTT EARTH
4 – NOT CONNECTED
5 – NOT CONNECTED

for a BNC or similar, though this will involve a bit of filing. The transmit audio has a characteristic 'tight trousers' effect from the external mike, due to its small enclosure.

Handheld
The handheld versions basically contain the bodyworn circuitry inside the case, but use a mechanical switch TX/RX change-over rather than a miniature relay, with the speaker/mike being internal to the set making the case size slightly longer. The transmit audio is improved over the bodyworn, and the set gives better communication range due to the requirement of you having to hold the rig to your face to talk, i.e. away from your body. This may of course be done with a bodyworn but would require two-handed operation as a result. The aerial socket is a standard-size TNC, again sometimes

Handheld 3-channel VHF set.

difficult to get hold of, but replacement with a BNC if necessary is mechanically easier due to similarity in size.

The PF5UH UHF handheld is a small handy size, although there is not much room inside for a toneburst unless you are good at miniature construction. The aerial is internal to the set, thereby giving slightly worse performance than an external one. This may be removed and a BNC fitted to the set top very easily if required, and may be a worthwhile improvement. The circuitry is similar to the PF2UH but with the absence of three channel capability.

Batteries

All sets use a similar 15 V nicad battery, and it is *very* important to ensure you get one of these included in the purchase, as spare batteries are often more rare than the sets themselves. Internally they are made up of several series-connected cells; if your battery is not charging or is only developing a low voltage then it may be prised open with care, and the faulty cell(s) identified and carefully

Single-channel UHF handheld—the PF5UH.

replaced, spare cells being available from Radiospares.

The batteries are rated at 200 mAh, and may be charged at a 20 mA rate. The two connections on the inner side of the battery are directly connected to positive and negative terminals. Those on the bottom of the battery are for use with the matching plug-in mains chargers which you may also be lucky enough to purchase on the surplus market. Note that for home use, a stabilised 13.8 V power supply is ideal for powering the set, a bodyworn equipment then making a useful 3 channel base rig.

Insides

Internally, the circuitry in each comprises several 'daughter' boards on a larger 'mother' board. This makes fault finding and component replacement fairly easy, as the boards may easily be desoldered if required. In the UHF sets there are two different types of receiver front end, passive and active. The passive one is fitted to earlier sets, and is identified by a rectangular metal block with two large tuning screws on top, forming miniature tunable cavities. The active front end is identified, simply, by the absence of the metal block, being replaced by a board with four small coil cans, one at each corner, with PTFE type tuning slug adjusters. The passive front end is good at getting rid of unwanted signals, and would therefore make a good 'listen-through' receiver, although it is slightly less sensitive than the active front end model. This may be worthwhile checking before purchase.

Crystals
The required crystal formulae are:

VHF

RECEIVER (2m)
$$\text{XTAL FREQ} = \frac{\text{CARRIER FREQ} + 23.455\,\text{MHz}}{2}$$

RECEIVER (4m)
$$\text{XTAL FREQ} = \frac{\text{CARRIER FREQ} + 23.455\,\text{MHz}}{3}$$

TRANSMITTER
$$\text{XTAL FREQ} = \frac{\text{CARRIER FREQ}}{12}$$

UHF

RECEIVER
$$\text{XTAL FREQ} = \frac{\text{CARRIER FREQ} - 23.455\,\text{MHz}}{5}$$

TRANSMITTER
$$\text{XTAL FREQ} = \frac{\text{CARRIER FREQ}}{27}$$

All crystals are HC18u type, with wire ends that are cut short so as to fit snugly into the small PCB mounted sockets.

There will be a 23.000 MHz crystal in each set, which is the receiver conversion crystal and should be left in place. In the 3 channel sets the crystals are located beneath the channel switch/RX I.F. screen. To remove this, first undo the channel switch nut carefully, then using a pair of long-nose pliers, remove the larger notched round nut securing the screen. Remove the screen, and fit the required crystals in the marked positions, replacing the screen later, of course. There will be a piece of insulated wire sticking out of a hole in the screen – remember to re-thread this through the hole as it will be used later.

On the PF5UH, the transmit crystal is plugged into the lower part of the set and is often visible, although sometimes it has a piece of sponge above it to hold it in place, hiding it from view. The receive crystal is beneath the RX I.F. screen, which may be removed by undoing the two or three screws and lifting off. Remember to rethread the insulated wire through the hole.

Alignment – UHF

The sets are made in two frequency ranges: 405–440 MHz and 440 MHz–470 MHz. Most of those available on the second-hand market in this country will be the latter of the two, but there is very little difference in circuit values between the two, and unless you wish to use the set below 433 MHz you would be very unlucky indeed if your set didn't tune down easily. I have never had any problems in over 50 sets, due to the built-in 'overlap' by the manufacturers. Sometimes the active front end tuning adjusters are right down at the bottom, as the coils are different between the bands, but reasonable sensitivity is still achieved and it is just not worth the complication of trying to change them for an extra dB or so in receive performance. The passive front end has no problem in covering right down beyond 430 MHz.

UHF TX Alignment

Initially, supply the set with 10 V only. If you only have 13.8 V or 15 V from the battery, then place a few diodes such as 1N4001s in series with the power leads to drop 0.6 V for each diode. Monitor the current taken with a multimeter, set at around the 100 mA range. Key the transmitter and tune 16L1, 16L2, 17L1 and 17L2 in that order for maximum current drawn. If you don't have a multimeter, then monitor the transmitter frequency on an adjacent 70 cm receiver, or one-third of the frequency on a 2 m receiver, and tune for maximum signal. You may like to do this even if you have a multimeter, to help you. When you have got an absolute maximum by tuning and retuning until you can't get any more, then you can increase the supply voltage to 13.8 V, or 15 V if you've only got the battery as a voltage source, and go on to the next step of tuning the P.A. Place a power meter in the aerial line, or look at the deflection on a field strength meter or similar. Using a larger non-metallic tool shaped as a flat-bladed screwdriver, tune 18C2, 18C7, 18C13 and 18C21 for maximum output, retuning as required for absolute maximum. These will each need about three or four turns clockwise to get onto 70 cm if initially aligned around 460 MHz. On the PF5UH tune 19C1 as a final step for maximum radiation when using the internal aerial.

The transmitter deviation will already be set to near the required amount, and I would recommend that you leave well alone. However for those with access to a suitable deviation meter who wish to set

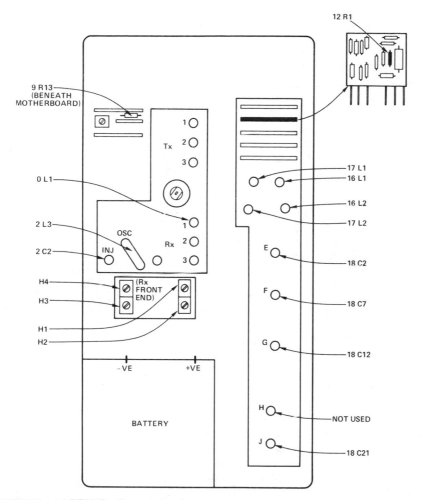

PF2UH and PF2UB alignment points.

their deviation to within that last half a kilohertz, a select-on-test resistor, 12R1, may be altered in value for the required level. Note that the microphone gain is a fixed level and may not be adjusted, this is a peak deviation adjustment only.

This concludes the TX power alignment, and you may now net the frequency by the trimmer next to the relevant TX crystal, repeating for each channel in turn.

UHF RX Alignment

This is where we need that bit of insulated wire poking out of the receiver. Connect a multimeter, set to the 10V range, with positive

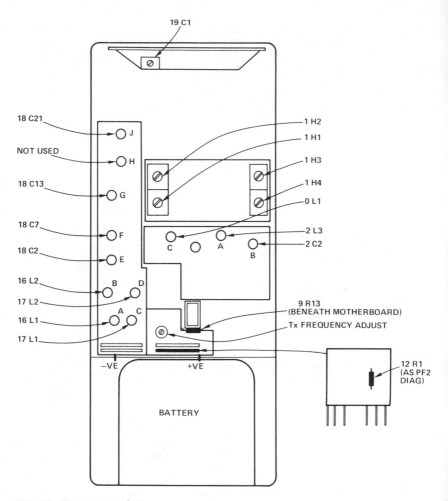

PF5UH alignment points.

connected to the wire and negative to any metal screen. With your ferrite coil adjustment tool, tune 2L3 for a dip in the meter reading, which will be at around three turns of the core into the former from being flush with the top.

Now get the receiver roughly on frequency by tuning the receive crystal trimmer 0L1, for best reception (least distortion) on a strong signal. In the active front end, use a flat-bladed adjuster and tune the four slugs, H1, 2, 3 and 4 for the best quieting signal. In the passive front end with the metal block, first loosen slightly the small locking screws in each of the adjusters, just enough to allow rotation of the two large adjusters, and then tune the two adjusters, not necessarily with a non-metallic tool, for the best quieting signal. Repeat the tuning of 2L3 for best dip and the front end alignment detailed as necessary to give absolute best sensitivity, and then carefully adjust 2C2 for the best quieting with the screwdriver-shaped tool. This tuning is sharp and there will be two tuning points, so choose the one which gives the best quieting. Now tune the receiver finally onto frequency by adjusting 0L1 for least distortion on a modulated signal.

VHF Sets

Channel Spacing
The channel spacing of the set, if not identified from the rear serial plate, may be found by removing the case front from the set and taking a look at the identification number of the metal crystal filter. This is marked with FC03262 or FC03246 for 12.5 kHz spacing, and FC03260 or FC03244 for 25 kHz spacing. Ensure the manufactured channel spacing of the set meets your needs, as replacement filters are fairly rare due to the uncommon first IF used.

Frequency Bands
The sets are manufactured in sub-bands of the standard A, B, and E bands, as well as the odd 'P' band set you may occasionally come across (which is of course best avoided). These are divided into:

E1 Band: 68–79 MHz
E2 Band: 77–88 MHz

B1 Band: 132–146 MHz
B2 Band: 142–156 MHz

A1 Band: 148–162 MHz
A2 Band: 160–174 MHz

You will find 'B' band equipments fairly rare on the UK surplus market, but 'A' band sets often tune to 2 m satisfactorily. Similarly with E2 band equipments for 4 m, although E1 band receivers will normally give better sensitivity. If, after following the alignment instructions, you find the set will not tune correctly, you may like to attempt the following capacitor changes:

E2 Band

RX RF Amp:	Change	C3 and C7 to 27pF
TX PA:	Change	C15 to 10pF
		C14 to 33pF
		C16 to 33pF

A2 Band

RX RF Amp: Change C1, C7 and C10 to 15pF

All these are small ceramic plate capacitors, readily available from suppliers such as Maplin and Cirkit. The RF Amp capacitors are located on the small front end 'daughter board', and you may find it easier to cut the existing capacitors to expose their leads, then carefully solder the new capacitors onto these, keeping all lead lengths as short as possible. Alternatively, you will need to carefully unsolder the eight leads connecting the PCB to the mother board, remove it and replace the capacitors.

Note that all the coils in the sets are common to both band ranges, and it is not necessary to replace or rewind any of these. Remember to try aligning the set before performing any modifications, to at least ensure it operates correctly. You may find it will perform very well without the need for any modifications whatsoever.

VHF RX Alignment

After installing your crystals as detailed, connect your power supply or battery and switch the set on. Connect your multimeter negative lead to the short length of insulated wire leading from beneath the hole marked OSC'. Now with your ferrite core adjusting tool, tune L3 and L2 on the Inj. Osc board for maximum dip in meter reading. We now need to initially 'net' the receiver onto frequency. Select the appropriate crystalled channel closest to the centre of your required frequency range, and by monitoring a received signal, tune the respective crystal trimmer for best reception, i.e. for least distortion on modulation. Once that has been done, on the RF Amp PCB tune T1, L1, L2 and T2 in that order for best quieting, repeating as required for the absolute best sensitivity.

After checking the crystal trimmer alignment again for correct on-frequency reception, you may also slightly retune L3 on the Inj. Osc board also for best quieting. There we are, that completes the receiver alignment. Return to the other crystalled channels, and tune their respective trimmers as required for the correct frequency.

VHF TX Alignment

Set your multimeter to a current range of around 200 mA, and connect in line with the voltage supply to the set, be this the battery (pull off the plug-in power lead on the board), or from an external 13.8 V power supply. If using the 15 V battery, if possible place a few diodes of sufficient current handling capacity, e.g. 1N4001s in line to reduce the voltage supplied to the set to 13.8 V initially. Place a

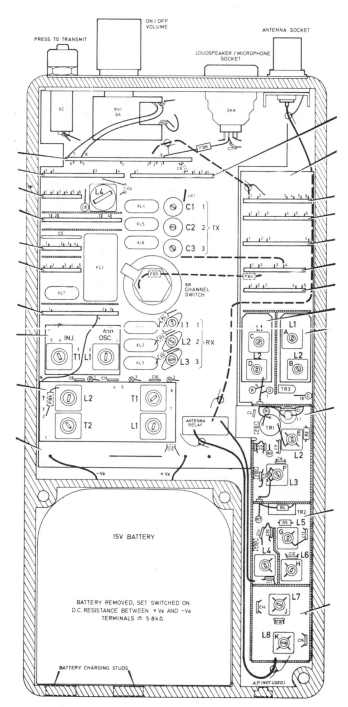

VHF FM pocketphone internal layout.

VHF FM pocketphone alignment points.

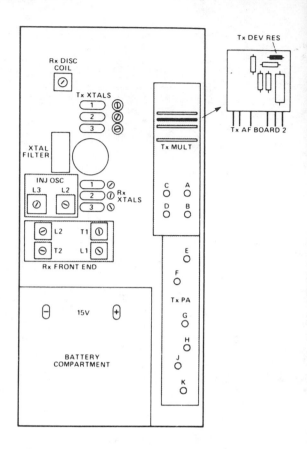

power meter in line with the aerial connection. If you don't have the correct TNC plug then simply unsolder the coax from the connection point to the socket on the inside of the case, with a further length of coax leading to your power meter. Remember to place a suitable load on the other end, a 47 ohm 0.5 W carbon resistor would prove suitable. Do not be tempted to operate the transmitter without a load or aerial connected, as you may seriously damage the PA stage.

Key the PTT, and with your ferrite adjusting tool tune the coils marked A, B, C, D, E, and F in that order for maximum indicated current, this may require you to select a higher current range towards the end. Retune as required for maximum current, or indeed maximum RF output if indicated. Now, monitoring the RF power output, tune the coils marked G, H, J and K for maximum RF, repeating as required for absolute maximum. In the higher power PF3FMH/B, J and K, which are low pass filter stages, are not fitted so don't worry if you find nothing to tune! Expect around 1.8 W output for the PF2, and around 2.5 W output for the PF3 model. If you need to reset the transmitter deviation, this is performed by changing the value of R3 on Board 12 of the transmitter modulator stages; increasing its value reduces the peak deviation. Access to this board entails melting the solder on the TX screening cover, and temporarily bending this back with a pair of pliers.

Before refitting the set's case lid, set the channel knob to the position of the channel selected to ensure the switch is not damaged when you reassemble the case.

Modifications

Apart from possibly replacing the set-top TNC aerial connector, if indeed this is required, you may find it useful to add a 'squelch defeat' button. An existing push-button is in fact sometimes fitted for sub-tone defeat, but if not you will find a suitable hole in the metalwork and plastic beneath the top trim. By using a switch to connect the R13/C1 junction on PCB 9 to chassis, the noise input to the squelch board is shorted to earth, hence activating the squelch opening circuitry.

The squelch is pre-set with the select-on-test resistor R13 on board 13 of both VHF and UHF sets, and normally should not require modification. However you may vary the squelch threshold by changing the value of this resistor, or in fact even fitting a small potentiometer in its place.

Faultfinding

From experience with these sets I have found that the vast majority of faults have been due to mechanical problems such as oxidised battery connections, a faulty on/off switch, and very often, intermittent operation of the small 'monitor' button. Sometimes solder joints between daughter board and mother board become open circuited from mechanical shock such as dropping the set, and in this case flexing the board gives intermittent operation. If this happens, carefully remove the main board – in the PF5UH by unscrewing the three retaining screws, in the PF2/3 series by removing the securing nuts on the controls – and carefully hinging the board out. Spend half an hour or so carefully resoldering all the connections, being wary of solder bridges, and you will often find this will cure most intermittent faults.

One fault I have found occurs on bodyworn equipments is that of an intermittent connection on the speaker mike, often when the strain-relief moulding has been removed. This invariably happens at the point where the multi-way lead comes out from the microphone plug. To cure this, you must carefully remove the lead by disassembling the plug, and I would advise cutting off the last 20 mm or so of lead, noting which colours of wire connect to which pins, then unsoldering them and discarding the short cut-off portion. Resolder the remaining lead and carefully reassemble the plug body, adding a length of thick heat-shrink sleeving if possible, to help prevent further problems.

SR1 PAGER RECEIVER

The SR1 is a VHF pager receiver, used mainly in the past by the UK fire service. When they became obsolete from the brigade, they flooded the surplus market in the same way as PF1 pocketfones did a short while before. I know of over 5000 SR1 receivers that have been released onto the market, a number having been sold at prices ranging from £1 to a few pounds each. By adding an off-the-shelf crystal and a cheap IC you can walk around monitoring your favourite local 2 m channel. If you're involved with Raynet or the like then change the crystal and add one capacitor to give you an emergency bleeper responding to a four second long 1750 Hz toneburst.

Circuitry

The pager itself is a complete receiver, with tone decoding and processing circuits added so it will respond to audio tones. It was not originally intended for voice reception, but may of course be modified to do so as I describe later. The accompanying block diagram shows what goes on inside the black box, where it can be seen that a standard FM receiver is used with demodulation down to audio performed in the usual way.

By removing the reed and placing an earphone across the diagonal contacts on the PCB reed socket you can in fact nicely hear what's going on, albeit without any squelch action to save you being deafened in the absence of signals. The receiver was designed to operate over the 142–174 MHz range, but all those I have seen on the surplus market have in fact been crystalled and tuned on 147.8 MHz, which is of course very close to 2 m. Two tone detectors are used, a resonant reed for the 'test' tone, and a tuned transformer for the 'alert' tone, used in combination with active buffers and diode detectors. The reed is encapsulated in a small rectangular metal case and plugs into a wired PCB socket in the receiver, resonating at a precise frequency in the range 600 Hz–1.6 kHz. Those found ex-service have normally used 600.9 Hz, 614.7 Hz, or 634.5 Hz, but you may find that some sets come sold with the reed removed. The transformer is a large ferrite cored affair mounted on the main board, a tunable core allowing fine variation in its resonant frequency. This is nearly always tuned to 3 kHz, employing a parallel

The SR1 pager receiver.

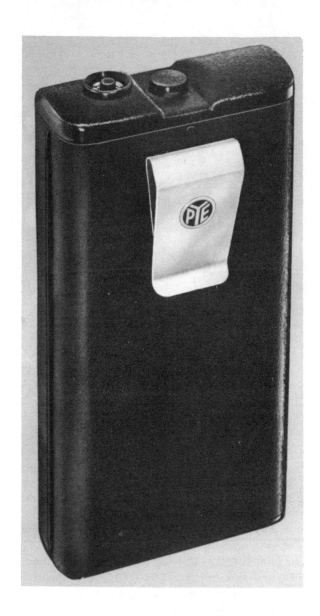

2nF capacitor, however some versions are fitted with a 2.3nF capacitor and tuned to 2.8 kHz.

Operation

In use, an RF carrier FM modulated with the test tone causes the pager to sound a constant audio tone from its small transducer, for a period of 20 seconds or until the reset button is pressed if sooner. If the RF modulating tone is then changed from the test tone to the

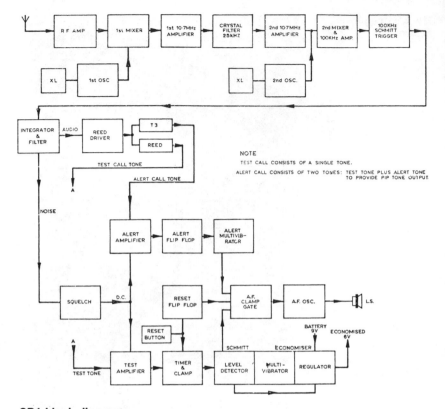

SR1 block diagram.

alert tone of 3 kHz, the pager alarm changes to an intermittent bleeping to warn of an emergency, this again lasting for 20 seconds unless reset. When first inserting the battery, a test alarm is automatically sounded by the pager to function as a battery check. There is no on/off switch, as for its intended use there was no need for one. An 80 mAh 8.4 V nicad is used, of the same dimensions as a PP3 and similar to the PF1 RX battery. Its life is extended by the use of an economizer, where the receiver is switched on for a few hundred milliseconds every two and a half seconds or so. This cycling action only stops when a test tone is detected to prevent continuous carriers draining the battery.

Conversion Possibilities

I will give details of two modifications, firstly a simple one of conversion into a 2 m pager, and secondly by adding an audio amplifier for conversion into a monitor receiver. Either modification may be performed, or of course if you're experienced in miniature wiring techniques then by adding a small switching circuit you can use it for both purposes. But first of all, let's get it going on 2 m, for which you need to get a crystal for the 2 m channel you want to operate on.

Crystals
The required overtone crystal frequency is:

$$\text{XTAL FREQ} = \frac{\text{RX FREQ} - 10.7\,\text{MHz}}{3}$$

A HC18/u (wire ended) crystal is normally used, however a more-commonly available HC25/u (pinned) crystal will fit if you don't mind cutting the pins short and soldering them in. These crystals are normally available from suppliers' ex-stock on popular 2 m frequencies.

Preliminaries
Remove the receiver board from its case by pressing the two upper notches inward with a couple of screwdriver blades or similar, while withdrawing the upper portion; an extra pair of hands is useful here! Desolder the 1st oscillator crystal if fitted, and replace it with your 2 m crystal. If using a HC25/u crystal you may find it convenient to solder thinner wires to the pins and solder these to the board rather than enlarge the PCB holes. Temporarily disable the timing circuitry by desoldering the pin 1 connection to the economizer, which may be easily done by bending back the lead on the printed circuit side of the motherboard.

Now connect an earphone or similar in parallel with a 390R resistor to the outermost diagonal pins on the reed socket, and find a reasonably local signal on your crystalled channel. In the absence of an external aerial connector, those with access to a low-leakage signal generator may couple the output to the capacitor connection between the ferrite rod sleeve and the motherboard. The receiver should already be fairly sensitive, but using a non-metallic trimming tool tune L2, T1, and L1 in that order for best reception. Note that L2 is the crystal trimmer, and you should adjust this first to obtain least distorted audio before any further adjustments.

On one or two sets, I found tuning T1 tended to send the set into self-oscillation, identified as a rapid quieting of background noise while drowning the wanted signal. Slight detuning of the core from its optimum position is required to effect a cure. T2 is the IF coil which should already been aligned and will not require trimming. Finally, move the outer metal slider of the ferrite rod aerial for best

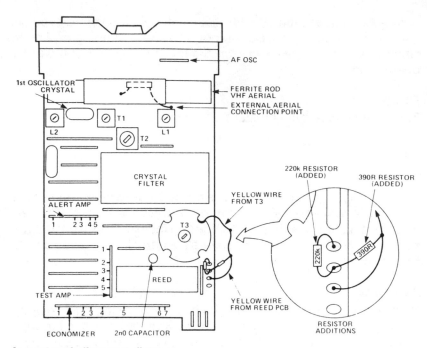

Layout and alignment diagram.

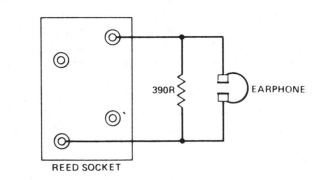

**Earphone monitor
connection.**

REED SOCKET

quieting on a weak off-air signal, this will normally have to be moved slightly to the right as viewed holding the set with the transducer at the top. Re-solder the economizer pin 1 connection, remove the earphone from the reed socket (but leaving the 390R resistor soldered in if no reed is fitted) and that's it, your set is fully aligned as far as its RF circuitry goes.

Tone Decoder Modification

If you are converting a number of these sets for group use, if all your

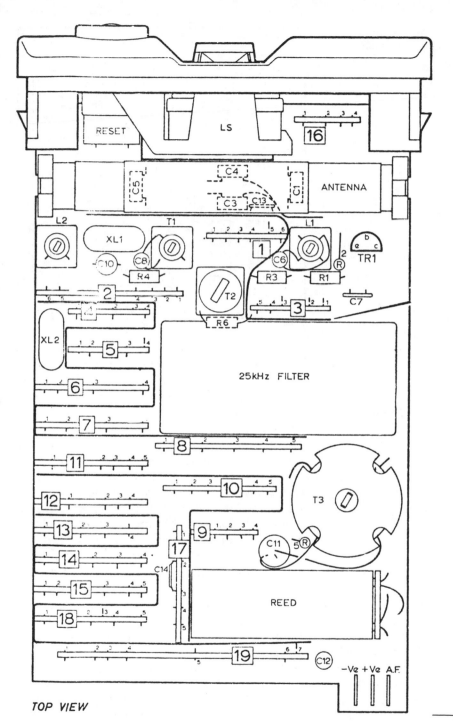

TOP VIEW

SR1 internal layout.

**Alert amplifier
board layout.**

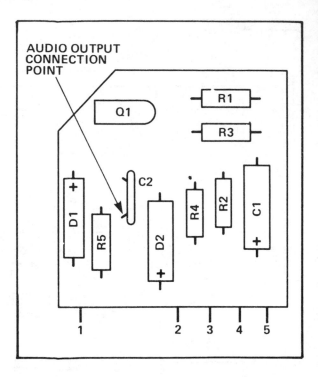

group's pagers have similar frequency reeds fitted and you wish to use them for their original purpose, then you may usefully skip the rest of the modification details. A test tone will be sounded following reception of a reed tone modulated signal lasting for 3–4 seconds, if this is followed by a 3 kHz modulated tone then an emergency alert will be sounded from the pagers. However as the pagers may come with no reeds fitted, and to save dedicated transmit tone generators, I thought it would be useful to detail modification to enable an alert to be sounded on reception of a long 1750 Hz tone, as many amateur FM sets have this facility available as standard on a push button.

A 5.87nF capacitance will resonate the tuned transformer to 1750 Hz. This can easily be performed by soldering a standard value 3.9nF polystyrene capacitor across the existing 2nF one, and tuning the core of T3 for the small amount of fine adjustment required. Remove the earphone if you have fitted this for monitoring purposes, but if doing so remember to keep the 390R resistor in circuit. Couple a high impedance AC millivoltmeter or more usefully an oscilloscope probe to pin 2 of the test amp board, failing this a DC voltmeter may be coupled to pin 4 of the test amp, which is the rectified output with a small DC offset superimposed. In either case, tune the core of T3 carefully for maximum reading when receiving a signal with an accurate 1750 Hz tone.

Now we need to make the set think it is receiving a test tone followed by an alert tone. Remove the two yellow wires leading from the reed PCB and from T3, and solder them together, insulated from any other board connection. Disconnect the brown wire from the reed board and connect it to this junction. Re-connect the 390R resistor to the rear of the motherboard as shown, and remove the remainder of the wires leading to the reed PCB and discard them. Connect a 220 K resistor as shown, this couples unfiltered audio to the alert amp board. Note that on some sets I have found that the required resistor value may need to be varied, depending upon the DC voltage gain spread of the following transistors, and you may need to vary this between 100 K–470 K for satisfactory performance. Once these mods have been performed, the test amplifier will become active on reception of a 1750 Hz tone (of a long enough duration to capture the economizer sampling period), hence sounding the test tone from the pager. The economizer will be defeated, and the alert amp placed into operation which will also detect the 1750 Hz tone and immediately switch the pager into alert mode.

Because only a single tone is being decoded, albeit using a very high-Q and hence narrow bandwidth filter, one must remember that false alerts may be possible with someone whistling, say, or a normal toneburst used on a repeater channel just happening to catch the sampling period of the economizer. For this reason it is preferable to use a 'quiet' channel for alert use. Remember also that some repeaters have a 1750 Hz notch filter in the through audio path which could influence use either way. I have found, even with the economizer disabled, that normal speech received on a simplex channel would rarely if ever trip the alert tone.

2 m Monitor Conversion

As unsquelched receiver audio is available from the set, if we tap in at a later squelched stage and suitably amplify the audio, then of course we have a normal voice receiver. Although it is possible to have the economizer running in this mode, the sampling interval of several seconds as used would cause the loss of the initial parts of transmissions or even complete loss of short calls. Rather than attempt to modify this for a shorter time with the result of diminishing returns, it is more suitable in practice to disable it completely. This may be performed by open circuiting Pin 1 on the economizer board, however this still keeps the economizer clock running with resultant quiet clicking noises superimposed on the audio, which could be a little annoying in use. Placing a positive bias on the clock 'hold' switching transistor base cures the problem, which is accomplished by connecting a 100 K (or thereabouts)

Economiser board linking details.

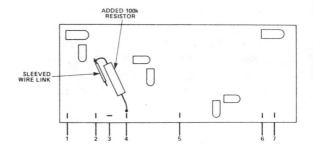

resistor between the Pin 4 connection and the sleeved wire link on the board.

High impedance squelched audio is available at the lower C2 connection on the alert amp board, and is the point immediately prior to it passing to the detector diodes for rectification. This connection will drive a high-impedance crystal earphone direct, but you will find insufficient level available if you try to drive a low-impedance earphone or speaker. Keen constructors may have their own ideas for a simple audio amplifier, however a small low-cost audio IC is widely available in the form of an LM386N which is ideal for this purpose. The accompanying diagram shows a copper matrix-board layout of a suitable amplifier circuit using this device, together with the circuit diagram itself. If a unit is constructed exactly as shown, the board will nicely fit in the space previously occupied by the test tone reed, its metal clip having also previously been carefully removed from the PCB. Component values are not particularly critical, 10 V working voltage electrolytic capacitors should however be used in as small a case size as possible. Don't be tempted to use lower voltage capacitors to obtain a smaller volume,

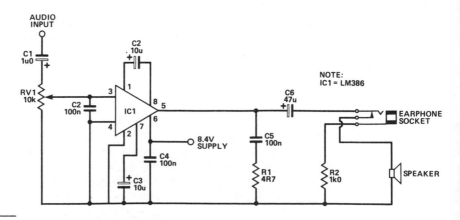

Audio amplifier circuit.

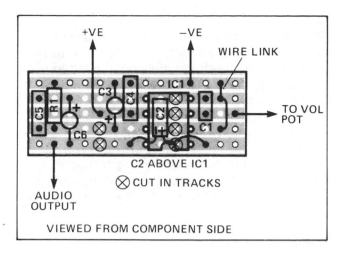

Audio amplifier copper matrix board layout.

+VE −VE WIRE LINK

IC1

C3 C4

C5 R1 C2

C6 C1

TO VOL POT

C2 ABOVE IC1

⊗ CUT IN TRACKS

AUDIO OUTPUT

VIEWED FROM COMPONENT SIDE

otherwise you'll find they tend to melt! The voltage supply may be taken from the adjacent battery terminal connections.

Under no-signal conditions, the amplifier draws only 5 mA, increasing with output volume of course when amplifying audio. The maximum audio output depends upon the individual type of LM386 used. It is available in LM386N-1, 2, or 4 suffices, the higher the suffix the higher the power, but even the lowest power will give over 400 mW RMS with an 8.4 V supply from the nicad, which is more than ample. There's only a small battery in there, remember, and using an earphone with a series 1 K resistor to earth (to stop you deafening yourself) will only result in around 12 mA current being drawn by the amplifier itself, the set drawing 20 mA typical.

The internal transducer may be used as a speaker, by disconnecting the four wires and using the black and white wires as speaker connections. You will however, find its quality extremely 'tinny', very similar to early Pye PF1 Pocketfone receivers fitted with a transducer. By removing the tuned transformer (replacing the primary winding, i.e. the two wires not connected to the 2nF capacitor, with a resistor of around 1K) and drilling holes in the case front to let the audio out, you may find enough room to fit a tiny speaker, the magnet fitting into the space vacated by the transformer. The small AF oscillator board at the top of the unit may be removed entirely, making room for a volume control or earphone socket if required, and the defeat button also may be removed to make further room, e.g. for an on/off switch if needed. I found a simple fixed resistor attenuator rather than a large volume control gave a useful compromise in space, using a 6k8 in series with a 3k3 to earth, the amplifier input being taken from the resistor junction in place of the volume control slider.

Uses

The modified set is small, light, and easily fits into an inside pocket or clips onto one's belt, making it a useful 'go everywhere' companion. Its use is certainly not limited to portable operation, in the shack it makes a useful monitor for the local chat channel whilst the main rig is used on another frequency. An external aerial, be this outdoor or a set-top helical to improve reception, may easily be used by fitting a single-hole BNC socket to the case top, connecting centre to the capacitor linking the ferrite rod sleeve to the PCB, with the outer of the connector going to the PCB earth plane. When testing in my shack, connecting a 500 mm long test lead to this point, showed the set was just as sensitive as my normal 2 m portable with its helical whip.

Batteries

You may also find suppliers are offering spare nicads at low prices and these are certainly worth taking advantage of. If you don't obtain a plug-in charger with the set (these again being sold very cheaply) then note that the required charging current is 8mA over a 14 hour

Plug-in chargers are also commonly available at very low prices on the surplus market.

period. The centre contact on the battery is positive, the outer two connectors are internally linked to the negative plate. Note that by using this arrangement it is impossible to insert the battery with the incorrect polarity. Using the set as a pager, plugging it into the matching charger overnight, will ensure continuous operation without the battery going flat. As a monitor receiver, expect around 3 hours use with an earphone, less when using a speaker, so spare nicads could be useful here.

Faultfinding

A large number of sets have been modified and found to operate satisfactorily. If you do have problems then the major cause of faults are dry joints between board pins and motherboard, an intermittent reset button, or more likely a faulty nicad in the first place, all easily rectified. Corroded contacts on the nicad or the connecting pins of the pager are a common case of intermittency so I would advise you to clean these as a matter of course. Due to the often extremely low price of these, I would recommend buying a spare set for the extra £1 or so rather than incurring a great deal of expense in trying to obtain spare parts for a faulty unit.

THE PF8 POCKETPHONE

This unit is a slim, single channel UHF transceiver employing an internal aerial at the top of the cabinet, and fits nicely into a top pocket. A transducer at the top of the set provides receiver audio, and a two-way PTT switch together with two internal microphones are used, one at the top and the other towards the bottom of the set, to enable it to be used either as a top-pocket portable or as a handheld unit held at face height for greater communication range. I have successfully used these in the past on 70 cm, and lately a number have started to appear onto the amateur surplus market at low prices. A transmitter power output of 500 mW is given, the set being powered from two 1.2V Ni-cad batteries used together with an internal voltage step-up inverter. It is important to ensure you obtain a set of these batteries when purchasing the transceiver, as they are otherwise fairly expensive to obtain, often costing more than the few pounds required for the set itself.

Crystals

The crystal can size used is the HC45/u size, a type of 'reduced height' HC18/u crystal. These are sometimes only available with a price premium, if you can only obtain the standard size variety then these may be used by leaving off the internal overall circuitry screen.

The PF8 pocketphone.

The crystal formulae required are:

$$\text{TX Xtal Freq} \quad = \quad \frac{\text{TX Freq}}{9}$$

$$\text{RX Xtal Freq} \quad = \quad \frac{\text{RX Freq} - 10.7\text{MHz}}{9}$$

Preliminaries

To remove the case, first side open the bottom metal cover and remove the batteries, inside here you will see a small slotted screw which must be removed. Then remove the two further screws on the side of the set, and slide the outer case away from the chassis. The overall screen is removed by unscrewing the small fixing screws, removing this will expose the crystals and the remainder of the internal circuitry. Fit your crystals, and connect a suitable 2.4 V power supply to the set, but *never* exceed a supply voltage of 2.7 V otherwise you're likely to damage the set's circuitry. The capacitor

Internal battery fitment

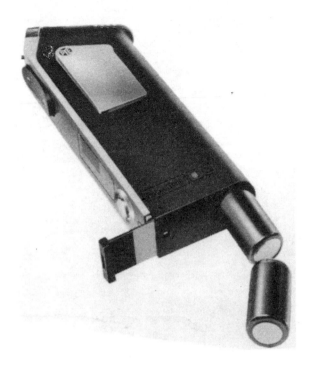

C69 is used only where the receiver frequency differs by more than 4 MHz from the transmitter frequency, for amateur 70 cm use this is not required hence it must be removed if it is present on your set.

Receiver Alignment

As a phase-lock loop receiver system is used, you will first need to adjust this section of the circuitry to ensure correct operation, however if the set came out of active service the adjustment of RV1 and L9 may not be necessary. If however, this requires setting, adjust the loop balance control, RV1, for 2.7 V indicated on a high impedance meter or DC coupled scope on pin 4 of the Thick Film module No. TF3 (MP6 on the diagram). Then while receiving a strong local signal on your required frequency, adjust the core of L9 until correct reception is obtained at mid-adjustment, alternatively with your high-impedance meter or scope adjust this for a 0 V average on pin 4 of TF3. You may also find by adjusting L6 you will 'centre' the receiver frequency correctly. Then remove the signal, and readjust RV3 if required for 2.7 V again on pin 4 of TF3, this completes the oscillator frequency setting.

Now connect your multimeter via a 10 k resistor to the emitter of TR3 (marked '4' on the diagram) and adjust L7 for minimum reading,

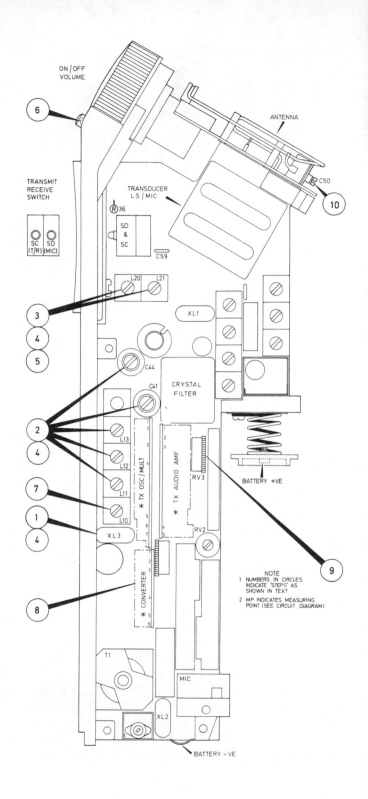

ON/OFF
VOLUME

ANTENNA

C50

TRANSMIT
RECEIVE
SWITCH

TRANSDUCER
L.S / MIC

®36

SC &
SD

SD
SC
(T/R)(MIC)

C59

L20 L21

XL1

C44

C41

CRYSTAL
FILTER

L13

* TX OSC / MULT

* TX AUDIO AMF

RV3

BATTERY +VE

L12

L11

L10

RV2

XL 3

NOTE
1 NUMBERS IN CIRCLES
INDICATE 'STEPS' AS
SHOWN IN TEXT
2 MP INDICATES MEASURING
POINT (SEE CIRCUIT DIAGRAM)

* CONVERTER

T1

MIC

XL2

**Receiver
alignment
points.**

BATTERY – VE

you should get around 5 V here. With your off-air signal, tune C50, L5, L4, L3, L2 and L1 for maximum sensitivity, indicated by maximum quieting, from the speaker, reducing the signal level as required to provide a suitable level of signal to noise ratio. Remember that L6 will have an effect also as previously stated. To adjust these coils you will need a screwdriver shaped non-metallic trimmer, a metal implement used here will significantly affect the tuning. When tuning to 70 cm, you will find that L1, L2 and L3 are often right at the bottom of their travels to achieve best sensitivity, and this may often provide a useful starting point when beginning alignment. If you have access to a signal generator, or you wish to connect an external aerial for tuning purposes, you may connect the coax link across the position of C69, marked on the diagram. Here you will find that C50, the internal aerial trimmer, will need final adjustment for best received sensitivity using an off-air signal picked up on the internal aerial.

RV1 sets the receiver squelch threshold, the small red 'defeat' button next to the stepped volume control acts as a squelch defeat when required.

Transmitter Alignment

Connect your multimeter, switched to the 1 A DC current range, in series with the 2.4 V DC supply to the set. With the transmitter keyed, tune L11, L12, L13, C41 and C44 for maximum indicated current. Now while monitoring the radiated RF level, adjust L20 and L21 on the aerial filter for maximum RF, then readjust L11, L12, L13, C41, C44, L20 and L1 again for absolute maximum. That completes the RF alignment, simple wasn't it? L10 sets the transmit frequency, which must be adjusted as required, and the potentiometer RV3 adjusts the transmitter peak deviation. Finally, slightly retuning the aerial trimmer C50 for maximum will ensure the greatest ERP, note however that the equipment case has an effect on this, hence a degree of trial-and-error would not go amiss here for best performance.

PF9 POCKETPHONES

These are separate UHF FM RX and TX handheld units, used in a similar manner to the PF1 TX/RX pair where the receiver is normally used clipped onto a lapel or in a top pocket, with the separate transmitter unit operated handheld when required. Due to the small size, the receiver makes an ideal monitor for your local UHF repeater, but if the associated transmitter is also obtained an effective transceiver combination results which is suitable for local UHF communication. The internal RF circuitry is similar in many

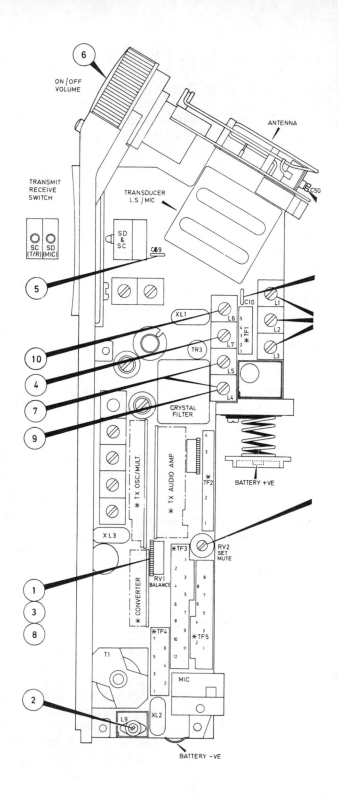

ON/OFF
VOLUME

ANTENNA

C50

TRANSMIT
RECEIVE
SWITCH

TRANSDUCER
L.S./MIC

SC
(T/R)

SD
(MIC)

SD
&
SC

C69

XL1

C10

L6

TF1

L1

L2

L3

TR3

L7

10

L5

4

L4

7

CRYSTAL
FILTER

9

TX OSC/MULT.

TX AUDIO AMP.

TF2

BATTERY +VE

XL3

RV1
BALANCE

TF3

RV2
SET
MUTE

1

3

CONVERTER

8

TF4

TF5

T1

MIC.

2

L9

XL2

BATTERY –VE

**Transmitter
alignment
points.**

PF9 pocketphones.

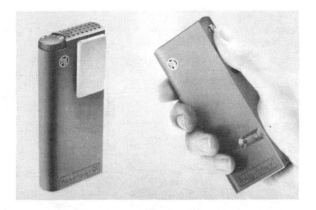

respects to the PF8 transceiver. Although these units are currently a little scarce on the amateur market, their advantages warrant a brief mention here.

Fitments
The frequency of the TX and RX is controlled by the crystal being used with small plug-in modules being employed, accessed by hinging open the battery lid at the bottom of the set. It is very important to ensure that these modules are included with the units, as they will *not* be capable of operation without them.

A single 1.2 V Ni-cad cell is used to power each unit, you will also find the commonly available 'AA' size Ni-Cad will fit into the battery opening and may hence be used if your set did not come with the standard PF9 battery.

To access the inner circuitry, first remove the volume knob in the case of the receiver, then on both the TX and RX units the inner assembly may be slid out from the case by hinging back the battery case cover as far as it will go, easing out the body of the set carefully.

Crystals
The crystals are fitted inside the plug-in modules. By carefully unsoldering the metal tags holding the small PCB to the metal body of this, the PCB may be removed to expose the crystal. Remove this and replace it with your 70 cm crystal, the formulae for these being:

$$\text{TX Xtal Freq} = \frac{\text{TX Freq}}{9}$$

$$\text{RX Xtal Freq} = \frac{\text{RX Freq} - 10.7\text{MHz}}{9}$$

Note you will need to use HC45/u case types, with their reduced

PF9 receiver alignment points.

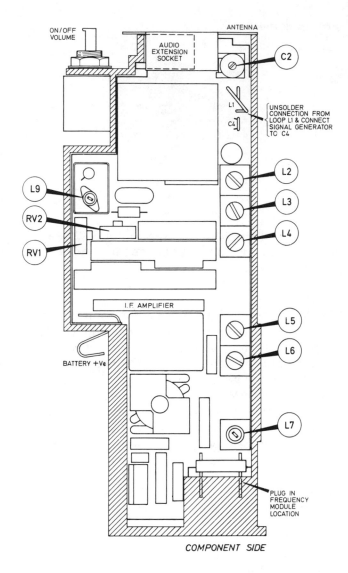

COMPONENT SIDE

height when compared to the more commonly available HC18/u versions, to ensure physical compatibility.

Receiver Alignment

With your set powered from 1.2 V DC, adjust the core of the small coil accessed through the bottom of the crystal module, for correct reception when receiving a strong off air signal, centring the adjustment of this as required. Then adjust the cores of L6, L5, L4, L3 and L2 in that order for best receive sensitivity, you may also find you need to adjust L7 for correct reception in practice. You'll find the

PF9 transmitter alignment points.

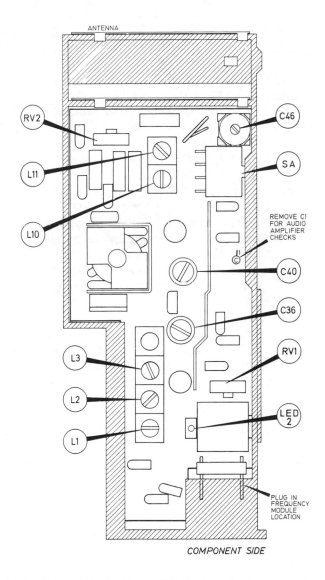

ANTENNA

RV2

C46

L11

S A

L10

REMOVE C1
FOR AUDIO
AMPLIFIER
CHECKS

C40

C36

L3

RV1

L2

LED 2

L1

PLUG IN
FREQUENCY
MODULE
LOCATION

COMPONENT SIDE

cores of L2, L3 and L4 will be at the bottom of their travel when tuned for best sensitivity on 70 cm, hence pre-setting them to these positions prior to tuning may prove beneficial. The squelch threshold is set by RV1, and as a final adjustment tune the aerial trimmer capacitor C2 for best sensitivity from a weak off-air signal. You may find the receiver case has an effect here, so trial-and-error methods are called for as with the PF8. A similar loop technique to the PF8 is also employed for the receiver. Adjustment of this should not normally be necessary but if required, RV1 is used to set the loop balance, with L9 being used for the 10.7 MHz VCXO.

Transmitter Alignment

With your plug-in frequency module in place, set your DC power supply to 1.0 V and connect your multimeter, set to the 1 A DC current range, in series with the supply to the set. With the PTT keyed, adjust the cores of L1, L2, L3, and capacitors C36 and C40 for maximum indicated current, then adjust the aerial filter coils L10 and L11 for maximum RF output on a field strength meter. Set the DC supply voltage to 0.9 V and readjust L1 and L2 again for maximum indicated RF. Now increase the DC supply to 1.15 V, and adjust L3, C36, C40, L10 and L11 for maximum RF radiated power. C46 is the aerial trimming capacitor, which must be adjusted for maximum radiated RF power with the transmitter case in place, again trial-and-error techniques are called for here. Finally to obtain the best efficiency and hence longer battery life, turn L10 clockwise and L11 anti-clockwise as far as possible *without* loss of RF power. RV1 sets the transmitter deviation, with the coil accessed through the bottom of the crystal module setting the TX frequency.

Toneburst Fitment

If you wish to fit a toneburst to the transmitter, don't be tempted to use the space available between the aerial upper and lower metal plates, this carries a high level of RF which will affect both the toneburst operation, and will also affect the aerial resonance hence reducing the radiated power. I have found by opening the legs of a 4060 CMOS IC and using 'flat' construction techniques, a toneburst as described in the 'Accessories' chapter will just about fit in the body of the transceiver if careful construction techniques are adopted. 9 V DC power is available on transmit on TP9 if required to power this.

6 FIXED STATION EQUIPMENT

Virtually any mobile equipment may be used as a fixed station of course, when coupled to a suitable 13.8 V power supply. In the past, suitable mains power supply modules were indeed manufactured to match mobile transceivers such as the Westminster and Europa series, to allow their use as a low-cost base station for users of small systems with a local operator and aerial system.

Remote Use

The equipment described in this chapter however is mainly concerned with dedicated base station equipment, normally operating from an AC mains supply and often designed to be used in a remote site such as a hill-top location, with remote control either over a dedicated UHF or SHF link or a hard-wired 600 ohm landline. Separate transmitter and receiver units are employed, these sometimes physically stacking above each other. An alternative type of lower-cost base station is a combined unit such as the F25FM or F9U wall-hung base station, with separate transmitter and receiver units employed but housed in the same cabinet.

To operate the base station, a desktop controller is used, this connecting to the other end of the remote wire or radio link. For local operation, for instance by the maintenance engineer, microphone connections together with a built-in or plug-in speaker are often fitted. Hence these base stations may be employed for amateur use without the further expense of a remote controller, these often being rare on the surplus market.

An exception to these VHF and UHF FM base stations is the SSB130 HF transceiver described at the end of this chapter. This is a 100 W LSB/USB/CW transceiver capable of operation from either mains or DC supplies that was originally designed for communication over long distances on HF frequencies. It has been included here as many amateurs will find it an ideal 'starter' base station for HF communication or as a dedicated unit for fixed frequency operation.

Local Use

Fixed station equipment occurs on the surplus market rather less frequently than mobiles or portables, simply because in service only one base station is used in combination with a large number of mobile or portable sets. Because of its normally higher cost and the inherent size, it is often more suitable for dedicated use such as for an amateur repeater rather than in an individual amateur's 'shack'. This may be either for voice repeater or for packet radio repeater use, and the facility of audio inputs and outputs at 600 ohm line levels permit interfacing to amateur-built repeater logic control and talkthrough switching circuits. Specific details on this use follow in the next chapter. For the average amateur however, base stations are sometimes useful as a 'dedicated' single-channel station. I have personally used a 2 m base station on 144.650 MHz linked to an SSB130 on 14.099 MHz through a packet radio TNC, to act as a dual band 'Node' providing a packet radio repeater service with cross-band gateway facilities.

Mobile Circuitry
Many fixed stations use similar board assemblies to those employed in mobile equipment, hence the alignment of these is essentially similar. In such cases, I will refer you to the relevant section on mobile equipment for RF alignment details.

F17FM

This VHF FM base station is made up of the R17FM receiver in combination with the T17FM transmitter, each unit being capable of independent operation if required. The individual units are supplied in 19 in. rack mounting format, but if you are lucky then you may see a pair together on the rally stand in a two-unit cabinet forming a self-contained assembly. The standard version is single channel, other versions allow local selection of up to six crystal channels. For remote use, a Radiotelephone Controller type T21 or PT RTC is required, these are however rarely seen on the surplus market.

The transmitter houses an AC mains supply for operation from 100–150 V and 190–250 V, 50–60 Hz, and this supplies a 24 V DC

The F17FM VHF FM base station.

supply to power the receiver. You may find receivers fitted either with just a DC supply input, or with a built-in AC supply for use independently from the transmitter PSU. The latter version is easily identified by removing the screens from the receiver case and taking a look to see if the clearly visible mains transformer is present at the rear, together with the small three-pin socket on the rear panel.

Identification

A look at the serial number label, fitted to the rear of the individual TX and RX units, will give details on the equipment frequency range and channel spacing. The units were made with three channel spacings, the most common of these being 25 kHz identified by 'V' on the label. Later 12.5 kHz models have an 'S', but you may also come across a very early type built for 50 kHz spacing identified by and 'N'. This is only of concern for amateur use in the case of the receiver, as we may simply adjust the transmitter deviation to whatever we like. Some units come equipped with a relay squelch output and talkthrough switching facilities. The relay squelch is useful for squelch line detection for packet radio use, or for repeater control, but talkthrough switching is of little relevance for our purposes.

Preliminaries

First of all, check the correct fuses are fitted. In the receiver FS1 is a 750 mA DC fuse, on the transmitter the marked DC fuse FS2 on the rear panel should have a 3 A fuse fitted. Ensure the correct marked voltage tappings on the AC mains transformer have been selected before you plug it in, checking also on the receiver if this is fitted with the optional AC power supply. When switching the power on, you may often find the small bulb behind the green plastic lens on the front panel of each unit does not light, this is very common due to their limited lifetime, and a quick check with your multimeter placed across the bulb DC connections will confirm whether all is OK.

If you find no audio output in the form of squelch noise is present on the receiver when you adjust the squelch control with the volume up, check that pins 3 and 4 on the tag strip TS1 are linked, these connecting the internal speaker into circuit.

Connections

The transmitter microphone may be connected to the rear panel socket SKB across pins 13 (centre) and 15 (shield), with transmitter PTT keying performed by linking pin 12 to pin 3 (0V common). The DC supply to the receiver if required, is present on pins 10 (positive) and 8 (negative), these must connect to the receiver chassis-mounted plug PLA pins 10 (positive) and 8 (negative). You may find

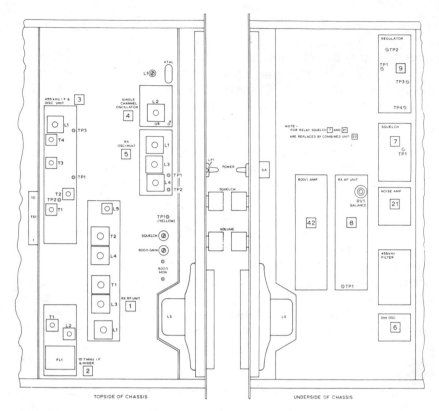

R17FM receiver internal layout.

plug-in crystal ovens used in the equipment to provide a high degree of frequency stability, in this case the TX socket SKB pins 2 and 4 must in turn be linked to the RX chassis plug PLB pins 2 and 4 to supply the DC voltage to operate the receiver oven. Pin 6 on each panel socket is connected to the respective TX and RX chassis.

In the case of multi-channel equipments, the channel change lines are 'slaved' via the multi-way 'channel' connectors on the rear panel. Pins 1–6 and 8 on the TX channel socket must be linked pin for pin to the RX channel socket for crystal switching to operate.

Alignment

The R17FM and the T17FM is based upon similar RF circuitry to the VHF Westminster series, and hence the alignment details for these, previously given in the chapter on mobile equipment, hold true. Remember that the unit is mains operated, so take care to keep your meter test leads away from the mains supply area. The crystal frequencies for both 4 m and 2 m are also identical, the crystals being plugged into their marked positions. Pin 3 on the transmitter socket SKB may be used for your multimeter 0V connection.

The receiver and transmitter should operate with a similar performance to the Westminster FM series, again if you wish to improve the receiver sensitivity you may change the RX front end transistors to J310s as detailed. You will find a large pre-set MIC GAIN potentiometer on the TX chassis which you may adjust to suit your microphone.

T30FM TRANSMITTER

This VHF FM transmitter is very similar to the T17FM, indeed looking identical from the front, however it has a different transmitter power amplifier supplied from 24V providing a higher output power in the order of 30W. It is often used in combination with the R17FM receiver, its similar rear pin connections enabling a plug-in replacement.

Identification
The T30FM can quickly be distinguished from the T17FM by the large screened TX power amplifier assembly present on the upper left hand side of the unit, this having several adjustment holes. The transmitter may be operated from AC mains of 100–150V or 190–240V, 50–60Hz, alternatively it may be fitted with a DC 24V input on the rear panel. Again the rear panel serial number plate will tell all, the transmitter having been manufactured in the following frequency bands:

Band	Frequency Range
H	29.7–38.6 MHz
G	38.6–50 MHz
E	68–88 MHz

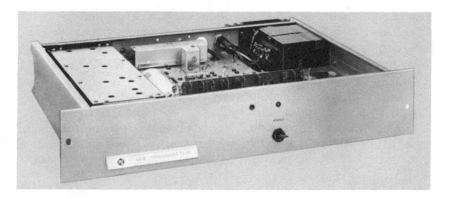

The T30FM.

P	79–101 MHz
B	132–156 MHz
A	148–174 MHz

Again, you will find the A band model will normally tune to 2 m with little difficulty, but do beware of the odd 'P' band equipment that may come up for sale, which uses a different multiplier and PA lineup that makes conversion uneconomic.

Crystals

HC6/u crystals are used, with the following multiplications:

$$\text{A, B bands} \quad \text{Xtal Freq} = \frac{\text{TX Freq}}{36}$$

$$\text{E band} \quad \text{Xtal Freq} = \frac{\text{TX Freq}}{24}$$

$$\text{G, H bands} \quad \text{Xtal Freq} = \frac{\text{TX Freq}}{12}$$

Preliminaries

Check the correct AC transformer tappings are in place for 240 V AC, and that the correct fuses are fitted, these being 2 A for the mains fuse FS1 and 10 A for the DC fuse FS2. Some transmitters have a 24 V DC supply input; for use instead with standby batteries in the event of mains failure, there should be a 10 A fuse in both positive and negative lines here. The microphone connects to the rear panel SKB socket pins 13 (centre) and 15 (screen), and PTT keying is performed by shorting pin 12 to pin 3 (0 V).

Alignment

The alignment of the initial multiplier stages is identical to those adjustments detailed for the FM Westminster range, where the coax link is disconnected from the PA and the multiplier tuned for maximum RF power output. The PA is however totally different, the alignment details for each band follow.

Initially set the chassis mounted potentiometer RV3 (marked 'RF Power) to give a multimeter reading of 24 V measured across the regulator pins 3 (positive) and 6 (negative) of the regulator PCB No. 9. Keep the transmitter keyed now for only as long as it takes to make adjustments, to save running the PA circuits in an untuned state.

A Band PA Initially set the trimmer capacitors as shown in the diagram, and note that the vanes of C9 must *not* be less than a quarter

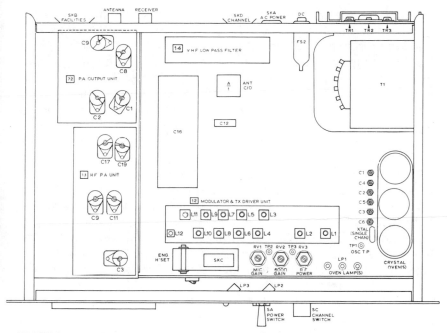

T30FM internal layout (A band).

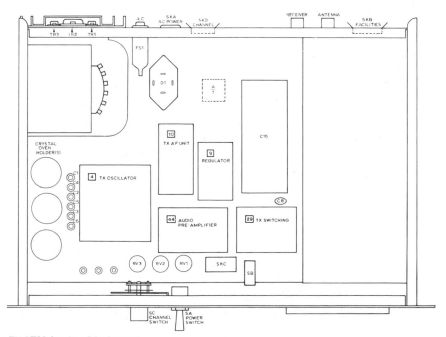

T30FM underside layout.

meshed. Remove the coax link between the first PA unit and the PA output unit, and connect your RF power meter and 50 ohm load to the output from the first unit. Connect your multimeter switched to a low DC voltage range with the positive lead to TP1, and the negative lead to the supply negative (SKB pin 3 or pin 8 of the driver PCB).

While keying the transmitter, tune C3 for maximum reading on your multimeter. Retune L11 and L12 on the driver PCB and then C3 again for maximum reading, you should get around 0.35 V. Change your multimeter DC voltage range to 15 V and transfer the positive meter lead to TP2, then tune C9 and C11 for maximum, retuning C3, C9 and C11 again as required to achieve absolute maximum. Now tune C17 and C19 together for maximum RF power output, retuning C3, C9, C11, C17 and C19 as required to give absolute maximum output again.

Reconnect the coax link, and transfer your RF meter and load to the rear panel aerial connector (*not* the adjacent 'RX' connector, an easy mistake to make!). If you have a diode probe, remove the PA cover and connect this to the junction of C4 and C5, tuning C1 and C2 for maximum reading, then tune C8 and C9 for maximum RF power at the aerial socket and replace the PA cover. If not, tune C1, C2, C8 and C9 carefully for maximum RF output power. Now repeat the tuning of all PA capacitors in both units for absolute maximum RF output, adjusting RV3 as necessary to keep the power output at the 30 W level.

B Band PA Set your multimeter to the 50 uA DC range, with its negative lead connected to the DC 0V line and positive to TP1 on the PA unit. Set all the trimmer capacitors to their mid-capacity positions as shown. While keying the transmitter, adjust C1 and C2 for maximum reading. Transfer your multimeter positive lead to TP2, and tune C3 and C4 both for maximum. Now transfer to TP3, and tune C5 and C6 for maximum reading, then tune C7 and C8 for maximum indicated

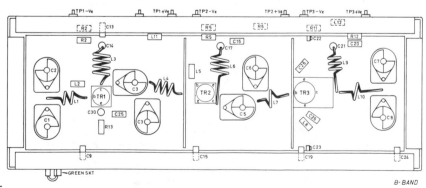

B-BAND

The T30FM B band PA alignment points.

RF power. You'll find it useful to use a pair of trimming tools here, one in each hand, adjusting capacitors in pairs for maximum power. Retune all these pairs of capacitors again for absolute maximum RF power, readjusting RV3 as required throughout the alignment to give an output power level of 30 W. If you cannot achieve 30 W you may find slight readjustment of L11 and L12 on the driver PCB called for.

E Band PA This is identical to the B band PA alignment, but instead adjusting C3 and C4 for TP1 indication, C5 and C6 for TP2 indication, and C7 and C8 for maximum RF output power.

G and H Band PAs If operating at the low frequency ends of these bands, e.g. the top section of 10 m, set RV3 to give 22 V rather than 24 V, otherwise continue as before. Initially set the vanes of trimmer capacitors C1, C5 and C7 about three-quarters meshed, and C2, C3 and C6 to minimum capacity, i.e. vanes fully apart. With your multimeter set to the 50 uA DC range, connect the negative lead to the

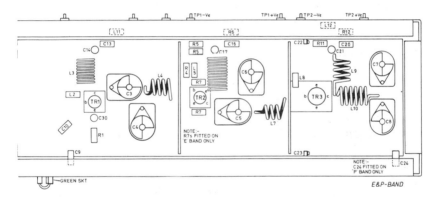

The T30FM E band PA alignment points.

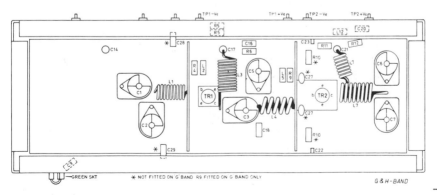

The T30FM G&H band PA alignment points.

0V DC line and the positive lead to TP1 on the PA unit. Whilst keying the transmitter, tune C2 for maximum indication, then gradually reduce the capacity (separate the vanes) of C1 while retuning C2 until you achieve maximum reading (10–15 uA). Retune L11 and L12 on the multiplier PCB if required for maximum indication.

Transfer your multimeter positive lead to TP2, tuning C3 for maximum and then gradually reducing the capacity of C5 while retuning C3 again for maximum (20–30 uA). Now tune C6 for maximum indicated RF power output, gradually reducing the capacity of C7 while retuning C6 for absolute maximum. Retune these capacitors as required until you achieve 30 W indicated RF power by final adjustment of C6.

This completes the RF alignment, remember to check your crystal frequency trimming, and set the chassis mounted MIC GAIN potentiometer to suit your microphone level. The rear panel mounted 'RX' aerial connector is coupled to an aerial change-over relay in the transmitter unit, switching this connector to the aerial coax when the transmitter is unkeyed. For normal simplex use, remember that you will need to add a short coax link cable to join this socket to the receiver aerial input connector.

R460 UHF FM RECEIVER

This receiver is often used in conjunction with the T462 transmitter, described later, to form a UHF remotely controlled base station. The standard receiver operates from a 24 V DC supply normally derived from the matching transmitter, alternatively it may be fitted with an

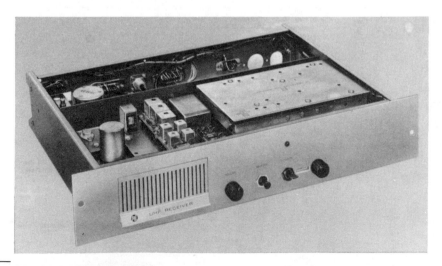

The R460 UHF FM receiver.

internal AC power supply to allow stand-alone use. It is built to be fitted to a standard 19 in. rack.

Much of the internal circuitry is based on the W15U Westminster, the front end stages however being dissimilar. Either single or 6 channel versions may be found. The crystals used are identical to those used in the W15U receiver. Remember to select the correct side injection as stated in the W15U information.

Identification

The receiver was manufactured in the following frequency bands:

T Band   380–440 MHz
U Band   440–470 MHz
W Band   470–500 MHz

The 'T' band model is fairly rare of course but is ideal for 70 cm, the more common 'U' band models will, however, tune down with care in alignment and with slight modifications in inductor coupling as I will describe. The W band units are very rare in the UK (I've never seen any – these normally being built for export) but do beware, this range is not suitable for 70 cm use. Inspection of the rear panel metal label is worthwhile as always.

The receivers were built for two channel spacings, very early sets for 'N' spacing, 50 kHz, later sets for 'V' spacing, 25 kHz. The latter is normally required for 70 cm use unless you're unlikely to suffer adjacent channel interference, i.e. from other repeaters or from the primary band users. Replacement crystal filters if required are available from the suppliers listed in the appendix.

Preliminaries

Check that the correct AC voltage tapping on the main transformer, if fitted, has been selected, and that you have selected the appropriate crystal position (this being 'slaved' from the transmitter in the case of multi-channel sets). On the tag strip TS1, pins 2 and 3 must be linked to connect the internal speaker into circuit, and pin 1 must be connected to 0 V to 'key' the receiver 'on'. Pin 17 is connected to the 24 V DC supply through the On/Off switch, with pin 14 connected to 0 V. When using the matching transmitter to supply 24 V DC power, the rear panel PLA chassis-mounted plug is used with pin 10 for the positive supply, pin 8 for negative. If a crystal oven is fitted, pins 2 and 4 on PLA must also be linked to the similar numbered pins on the transmitter socket to supply power to the oven.

Alignment

You will need to make up a short RF 'probe', such as a short length of

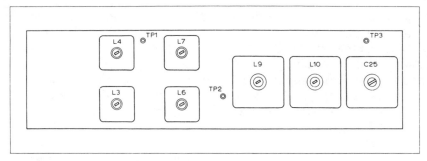

R460 Oscillator multiplier alignment points.

coax with an exposed centre core of around 1 in. long, this coax being connected to your aerial or signal generator output during the later alignment stages. However first connect your multimeter, set to the 250 uA DC range, with its positive lead to TP1 on the oscillator/multiplier PCB (board 5) and the negative lead to the DC supply negative (TP2 on the 455 kHz IF PCB, board 3, is 0 V). On board 5, tune the cores of L3 and L4 with your ferrite core adjustment tool for maximum current reading. Transfer the positive lead to TP2 on this board, and adjust L6 and L7 again for maximum, retuning L3 and L4 slightly as required for absolute maximum. Transfer to TP3, and tune L9 and L10 again for maximum, then with a non-metallic trimmer adjust C25 for minimum reading. Keeping your multimeter connected to TP3, locate C20 on the large RF Amplifier unit and adjust C20 for maximum current reading. Transfer the multimeter positive lead to TP1 on the RF bias chain unit, board 36, and tune C19 on the RF Amplifier for maximum reading. Readjust C25 on board 5, and C20 and C19 both on the RF Amplifier board slightly as required to give absolute maximum current reading on this test point.

Now on the RF Amplifier board, adjust C1, C8, C9, C13 and C16 initially to maximum capacity, i.e. with their vanes fully meshed. During alignment, keep the lid of this board in place, you should be able to see the positions of the capacitor vanes through their respective adjustment holes. If you do remove it, you'll find you may need to readjust C19 and C20. During alignment, you'll need to insert the end of your short RF probe to touch the rotors of the various capacitors, so each section of the receiver front end can be aligned stage by stage. If you connect the positive lead of your multimeter, set to the 2.5 V DC range, to TP1 on the 455 kHz unit, you may use this as a signal strength indicator to aid tuning, keeping the received signal at a suitable level to indicate around 0.7 V at each tuning stage.

Using your RF probe carrying a strong signal on the correct

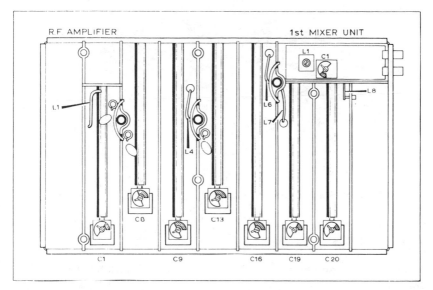

R460 receiver front end internal layout.

frequency, place this on the rotor of C16 and initially tune your crystal trimmer for reception on the correct frequency, then tune C1 for maximum signal. Place the probe on the rotor of C13, and tune C16 for maximum signal, then with the probe on the rotor of C9 tune C13 for best signal. Finally, transfer the probe to the rotor of C8, and tune C9 for best signal. You should now be able to receive a signal via the rear panel aerial socket, tuning C8 and C1 for best signal, then readjusting all the other trimmers slightly as required for absolute best sensitivity on a weak signal. Finally trim your crystal adjuster for spot-on frequency, TP3 on the 455 kHz IF PCB carries a 'centre zero' voltage which may be used for precise netting from an off-air signal of known accuracy.

Sensitivity Improvements

If after carrying out the alignment carefully, you find the sensitivity is not up to scratch, and the original receive frequency was far removed from 70 cm, it would be worthwhile to adjust the RF coupling in the front end stages. With the lid of this removed, adjust the positions of L6, L4 and L1 as required – you will have to experiment a little to obtain the best sensitivity. Often moving these inductors just slightly closer to the capacitor-tuned lines will provide an improvement when retuning to 70 cm from a higher frequency. Remember to replace the lid and slightly retune after each adjustment.

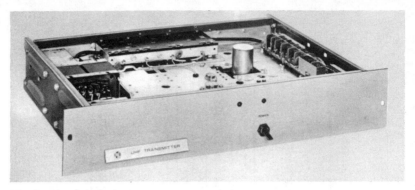

The T462 UHF FM Transmitter.

T462 UHF FM TRANSMITTER

This unit is often used as an accompanying transmitter to the R460 receiver. It is built to fit a 19 in. rack, and operates from an AC mains supply of 110–240 V, 50–60 Hz, or 24 V depending upon the original option built. Single channel units are the most common, but six channel units with manual channel selection have also been made. When used with the companion receiver, the AC mains supply of the T462 supplies 24 V DC to power the receiver. The RF stages are similar to the W15U UHF Westminster transmitter, with similar alignment requirements.

Preliminaries

Check that the correct AC mains transformer tappings have been selected, and that the rear panel mounted AC (2 A) and DC (5 A) fuses are in place. The microphone may be connected to the rear panel SKB socket across pins 13 (centre) and 15 (earth). TX keying is performed by shorting SKB pins 12 and 3 together, pin 3 being chassis. Most sets found in the UK operate with a negative switching line, this is identified by the connection between SKB pin 12 to pin 5 on the Switching PCB board 29, a connection to pin 4 on this board giving positive switching. Positive 24 V DC power to the receiver is present on SKB pin 10, with negative on pin 8. If using a multi-channel set, a further 'Channel' connector SKD will be found on the rear panel, this carries switching liners to a multi-channel receiver, and these sockets must be linked pin for pin.

Alignment

The crystals required for this transmitter are identical in frequency and loading specification to the W15U UHF Westminster. Likewise, the RF alignment details are identical and I hence refer readers to

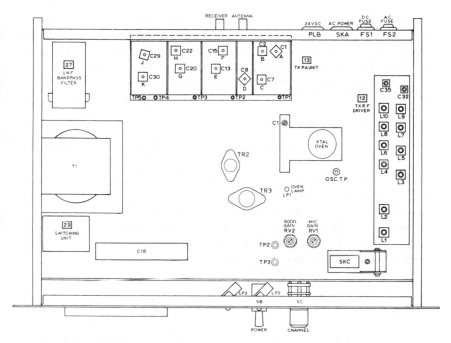

T462 alignment points.

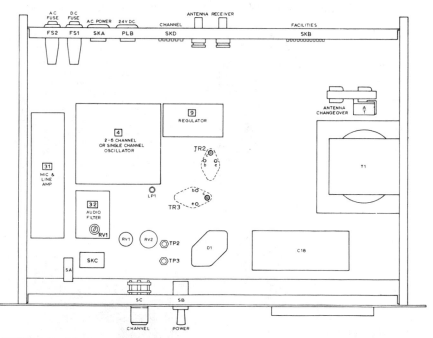

T462 underside chassis layout.

the relevant section of this book for information. A modified crystal oscillator is used however, this having a tunable ferrite core for output adjustment and this must be tuned for maximum voltage on the first TX multiplier test point, followed by L1 and L2 on the multiplier board as for W15U alignment.

F25FM AND F9U/L9U

These base stations are based on 'Europa' mobile transceiver RF PCBs, using the MF25FM circuits for the 25 W FM F25FM base station, and the MF5U circuits for the 5 W UHF F9U base station and L9U link station. The frequency bands, channel spacings etc. are hence identical to these equipments and I refer readers to the section on these mobile sets for performance and alignment information. They are now becoming commonly available on the surplus market, and make a reasonable transceiver for base station simplex use without the need for a separate AC supply.

Identification
They are built as reasonably slim 'wall hung' units, identified by their light blue overall cover, housing separate transmitter and receiver PCBs mounted side-by-side onto the chassis. A mains power supply and transformer is added, together with a 'remote' module for

F25FM and F9U/ L9U wall-mounted base station.

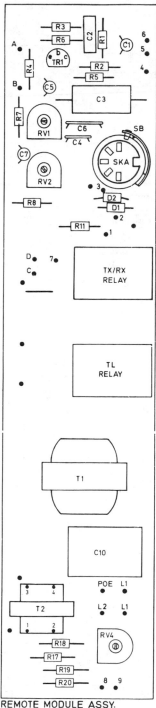

REMOTE MODULE ASSY.
VIEW THROUGH BOARD

Remote control PCB module.

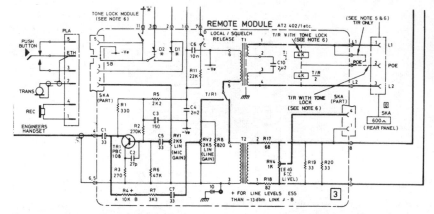

Remote control module circuit.

600 ohm line control. Depending upon the original requirement, they may be fitted with separate aerial sockets for duplex use, or a combined TX/RX aerial socket fed from a coaxial change-over relay for simplex use. Either may be simply modified to suit whichever purpose you require by suitable additions.

Connections

The 'Engineer's Handset' socket, SKA, is the most useful here, this is a standard 180 deg. DIN plug with the shield connection also used. You will find loudspeaker output across pins 4 and 1, but note this is a floating line, neither must be connected to earth as detailed in the mobile information. RV4 on the receiver PCB acts as the receiver

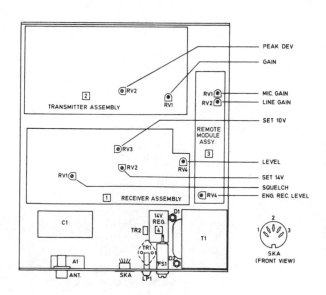

The F25FM internal layout.

pre-set volume control, which you may like to replace with a chassis-mounted 10K potentiometer for manual control. The microphone input is connected across pins 2 (centre) and the outer plug connection (shield) which is the chassis 0V connection. A change-over switch connecting Pins 5 (RX) and 3 (TX) to this shield provides TX/RX change-over – note that it is possible to have simultaneous TX and RX operation for duplex use by connecting both to the 0V shield.

There is little more to say regarding this equipment due to its similarities with the mobile transceivers, however the following chapter gives further details as to their suitability for repeater usage. Do check though for the correct mains transformer tappings, and that suitable fuse ratings are fitted before plugging into the mains.

THE SSB-130 100 W HF TRANSCEIVER

Many amateurs consider ex two-way professional gear to be VHF and UHF only, operating solely on AM or FM. Not so, if you know where to look you'll find a 'blue box' with the label of 'SSB130' on it; at one rally for instance a number of these were being sold from £50 upwards by one trader. In common with most other ex PMR gear it operates on several crystal controlled channels, great for net use but I'll also be showing how to incorporate at VFO or synthesizer add-on to give greater flexibility. I have used an SSB 130 now over 5 years: as

The SSB130 transceiver.

well as providing many pleasant SSB contacts on 80 m and 40 m it has also been used for the HF port of a HF/VHF packet radio node, allowing the main transceiver to be freed for other uses when required.

Features

The set covers 2 MHz to 15 MHz in three pre-set ranges, and was built to operate on six crystal-controlled channels each operating on USB, LSB, CW, or SSB with inserted carrier to provide AM. Plug-in power supplies allow operation either from the AC mains, or from 12 V or 24 V DC supplies for mobile or remote use. A pair of 6883B power tetrodes are used in the final transmitter amplifier to provide an output of 100 W peak envelope power, the remainder of the set being solid-state. Six SO-239 coax aerial connectors on the rear of the set allow you to connect separate aerials for each frequency range if needed, you can of course common any or all of these up as required for multi-band use.

There are two versions of the set, the most common being the SSB 130M designed primarily for mobile operation. This features a built-in speaker, volume and squelch controls, mode switch, a large six-channel knob, and a 'trim' control acting as a receiver clarifier (RIT). A small control box may be connected if required to enable the relatively large set to be mounted remotely in the vehicle. The SSB130F is similar to the 130 M apart from having an elongated facia housing a metering panel and VOX facilities. The DC power supply

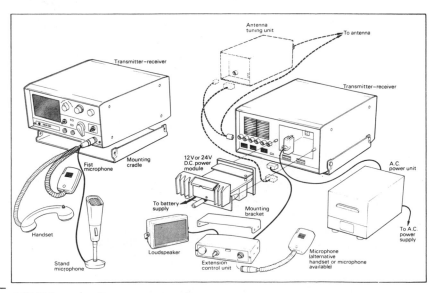

SSB130 connection arrangements.

Rear view showing space for the plug-in DC power supply unit.

The SSB130 mains
power supply unit.

fits into an opening at the rear of the set, note that *different* plug-in
units are used for 12 V and 24 V although these appear physically
similar – look at the attached metal label riveted onto the unit to
check. The AC supply comes in a black case fitted with a thick multi-
way lead plugging into the rear PSU opening in the SSB130. Make
sure when purchasing your SSB130 that you also obtain a power
supply, these sometimes being sold separately.

Frequency

As you will see, the set may be used to cover the 80 m, 40 m, 30 m and 20 m amateur bands, and with a bit of 'stretching' the top section of 160 m if required. It is important to note that each batch of sets were individually made to order, and that you will find each switched channel position corresponds to a given built-in frequency range. These are divided into three bands:

LOW: 2 MHz–4 MHz
MID: 4 MHz–8 MHz
HIGH: 8 MHz–15 MHz

Any particular channel fitted and aligned in the equipment within a given range may be changed at will with a crystal change and retune but *only* to another frequency *within* that range.

Internal view showing the round crystal oven unit on the left.

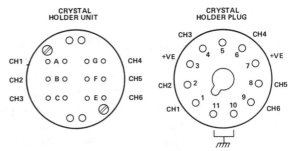

CRYSTAL HOLDER UNIT

CRYSTAL HOLDER PLUG

Crystal oven pin arrangement.

5-PIN 270° DIN PLUG

1 = MIC LIVE
2 = MIC SCREEN
3 = PTT
5 = PTT

**Microphone
connections.**

You may find that many sets will come fitted with at least one channel in each range, to allow the original user the maximum versatility in choice of operating frequency dependant upon the prevailing propagation conditions from tlme to time. This of course will also give you the best flexibility, but I have seen the odd one or two sets with only the 'Low' and 'Mid' ranges fitted, so beware. The operating frequencies are often marked on a label affixed to the front or rear of the set, if not I would advise a quick look inside the covers to see which frequency ranges are provided.

Identification

To check which ranges are fitted, first look for any frequency label, even if this is out of date due to re-crystalling from change of use it would still have been correct at one time, giving a reliable indication unless the equipment was internally rebuilt– a rare occurrence. Of course not all six channels may have been used, so take the lid off the set and look at the identification part numbers of PCB No. 85 (three of them, side by side). These are the TX/RX common tuned circuits with each PCB covering two channels. From these you will identify:

Assembly Part No.	Bands Covered
AT27112/1	LOW/LOW
AT27112/2	MID/MID
AT27112/3	LOW/MID
AT27112/4	MID/HIGH
AT27112/5	HIGH/MID
AT27112/6	HIGH/HIGH
AT27112/7	LOW/HIGH

A further check may be made of the three TX tuned circuits, identified as PCB No. 82, these being:

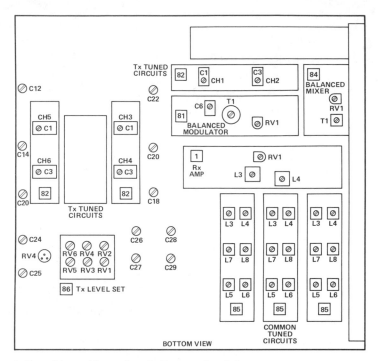

Internal board layout and alignment points.

Assembly Part No.	Bands Covered
AT27111/1	LOW/LOW
AT27111/2	MID/MID
AT27111/3	LOW/MID
AT27111/4	MID/HIGH
AT27111/5	HIGH/MID
AT27111/6	HIGH/HIGH
AT27111/7	LOW/HIGH

As the set operates as a single conversion TX/RX, with an intermediate frequency of 1.4 MHz, you will need a crystal exactly 1.4 MHz higher than each of your intended operating frequencies, conversely if the original crystals are fitted these will show you the operating frequencies of the equipment as supplied. So while at the rally, equipment sale or dealers' premises where you bargain for your SSB130, keep a lookout also for boxes of surplus crystals on sale. At least one crystal on each band will certainly act as a starting point to help you get the transceiver tuned up as well as providing many QSOs following your CQ call if the crystals operate in a suitable portion of the amateur band.

Tuning Up

First of all, fit your crystals, remembering to place these in the correct channel positions for the frequency ranges fitted in your particular set. If the plug-in crystal housing has been removed, or your crystals are of a different holder size, you may find it convenient to mount suitable sockets onto a piece of Veroboard or similar, wiring these to the underside of the original crystal socket. Each aerial socket is numerically marked corresponding to the channel number, if you wish to use a single aerial for all bands simply link all the socket centre pins together inside the set with a soldered length of wire.

Switch the set onto receive, with the volume control mid-way and the squelch control to the fully 'off' position. You'll need some form of HF signal source to align the receiver, and you'll need to reduce the level of this as tuning progresses. A purpose-designed signal generator is ideal of course, alternatively a strong off-air signal from a local amateur could be used, combined with reduction of transmitter power or variation of your receive aerial length or attenuation. I have even had complete success in the past simply by using a small handheld 1 kHz signal injector into the aerial socket to align an SSB130 onto 80 m, the generated square wave of this being rich in harmonics right up to HF.

Receiver Alignment

By injecting a strong signal at the required receive frequency, remembering to use the correct aerial socket if these have not been linked, you should hear a beat tone coming from the speaker. All you need do now is simply tune the receiver stages for maximum audio level, reducing the RF signal level as required. To do this, on the common tuned circuit board (PCB No. 85), tune L6, L8, and L4 if using channel 1, 3, or 5, alternatively tune L5, L7 and L3 if using channel 2, 4 or 6, remembering to adjust the correct bank of coils appropriate to your selected frequency range. Retune these again as required for the absolute best sensitivity. Having done that, you may now peak L3, L4, and RV1 on the receiver front end board (PCB No. 1), and T1 on the balanced modulator board (PCB No. 81), all for absolute best sensitivity, these last adjustments however should need little alteration if the set has been in previous use. Alignment of the common tuned circuits, ie. L6, L8, and L4, or L5, L7 and L3 must now be repeated for each fitted channel, remembering that each crystal position has its own tuned circuit line-up.

Transmitter Alignment

Initially turn the chassis-mounted capacitors C24, C25, C26, C27, C28 and C29 all fully clockwise, and on the TX level set board (PCB

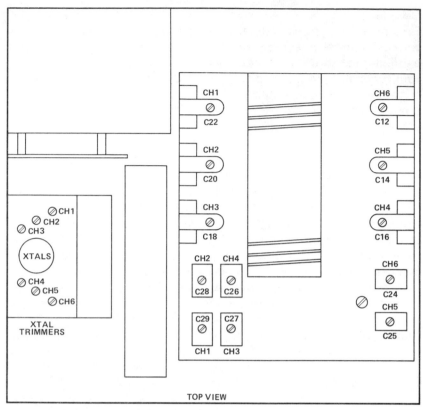

Transmitter power amplifier alignment points.

No. 86) turn RV1, RV2, RV3, RV4, RV5 and RV6 all fully clockwise. Then set the TX PA coil tapping points as shown, ensuring the correct link is used for each crystal position with its respective frequency range. You'll need a power meter and suitable 50 ohm load connected to the relevant aerial socket to provide an indication of transmit power, remembering to allow for the 100 W power generated, and a simple multimeter for tuning adjustments.

TX PA Tapping Points

Band	No. of Turns	
160 m	27	(Max)
80 m	18	
40 m	11	
30 m	9	
20 m	6	

Place the Mode switch onto LSB or USB, and connect your multimeter set to the 10 V DC range between the power supply unit sockets TP1 and TP2. Operate the microphone PTT and adjust RV4, mounted on the chassis, for a multimeter reading of 0.8 V. Now place the mode switch onto one of the CW positions, keeping the PTT depressed. On the transmitter tuned circuit board, (PCB No. 82), adjust the appropriate C1 or C3 capacitor (C1 for channels 1, 3 and 5, C3 for channels 2, 4, and 6) for a meter reading of 1.5 V. Then adjust C22 (Ch.1), C20 (Ch.2), C18 (Ch.3), C16 (Ch.4), C14 (Ch.5), or C12 (Ch.6) as appropriate for a 'dip' indication on the multimeter, repeating these last two adjustments as required for the greatest dip.

By now you should be seeing some RF being indicated on your in-line power meter. Adjust C24–C29 as appropriate for your switched channel to obtain maximum RF power, then adjust C22–C12 again for maximum dip on the multimeter, note that the multimeter reading shouldn't exceed 3 V here. On the balanced mixer board (PCB No. 84), adjust T1 for maximum reading, and continue readjusting these two capacitors as required for maximum voltage reading, this should give around 2.6 V when using a DC PSU and 2.9 V with an AC PSU. Now turn the relevant TX level set potentiometer RV1–6 down until your multimeter reading drops by 0.1 V to avoid over-driving in use.

This procedure will again need to be repeated for each crystal position, tuning the appropriate capacitors in each case. You should find your set will now give you around 100 W on CW and SSB transmission, and as a final adjustment switch the mode knob to one of the AM positions and adjust RV1 on the balanced modulator board until the indicated RF output is 25 W. That completes the transmitter alignment, all that remains to be done is any slight 'tweak' of the appropriate crystal trimmer to place you on the exact frequency you require, you'll find this has a tuning range of anywhere between 0.5 kHz and 2.5 kHz depending on the frequency in use. Remember when doing this to place the front panel 'trim' control at centre position.

That completes the alignment, all you need do now is connect your aerial plus any tuning unit if required. The PA is reasonably tolerant of impedance mismatch, certainly far more so than many home-brew solid state PAs of this power level. Any low impedance dynamic microphone giving around 5–10 mV output will be suitable, and the standard 5-pin DIN connector is used.

Modifications

You may find it useful to extend the crystal socket connections onto the front of the set, together with a front-panel mounted variable capacitor for frequency trimming, to save you repeatedly diving into the set with your screwdriver to net onto the station, calling CQ just half a kHz or so off your frequency (yes, I've had my fair share of doing that!). Alternatively, you may consider building a small VFO to allow continuous coverage. Remember the VFO or crystal frequency required is always 1.4 MHz above the final RF frequency, so you'll need to band switch your VFO as well between ranges.

Tunable Additions

A useful addition could be the 'Minisynth PLL VFO' from Cirkit, the basic kit (Stock No. 41-03300) currently selling at under £25. This uses a stable low frequency reference VFO operating at under 1 MHz and tunable over the band of interest, controlling a final frequency VCO (Voltage Controlled Oscillator) producing a low noise signal that could possibly be of benefit over a synthesizer approach on our congested HF bands. A variable capacitor and reduction drive is supplied with the basic kit, a further mixing crystal and small number of components are required for each band of interest. Hence by using this approach one can build an accurate multi-band VFO to control your SSB130, using the front-panel crystal switch simply as a band change as a result. The VFO output is simply fed to the crystal socket connections.

Alternatively, the technical boffins may wish to add a digital synthesiser. Again Cirkit offer the MC145151 Development Kit, (Stock No. 40-14151) currently selling at just under £20. This covers 4–6 MHz as supplied, and as such may be used for the 80 m band, alternatively a few component changes will enable it to be used on any or all of the other bands. Simple DIP switch lines are used for frequency control, and tuning methods are limited only by your imagination, such as diode arrays for fixed net channels, or optical couplers for up/down control. Using the supplied crystal, 10 kHz steps are provided, smaller steps down to 625 Hz may be used simply by reference link changes and appropriate alteration of the low pass filter component values if required. Interpolation between these steps may be performed by varying the trimmer capacitor across the reference crystal.

7   TALKTHROUGH REPEATER CONVERSIONS

In this chapter we deal with the requirements for operating equipment as a talkthrough repeater. This function is completely different from operation as a packet radio repeater. In the latter case the transceiver whether mobile, base or portable, can often be used normally, due to the simplex nature of the mode, with no modifications required.

As a talkthrough unit, the receiver operates *at the same time* as the transmitter, using a different frequency but normally within the same band. The receiver operates continuously, as soon as a valid signal is received the transmitter relays this received signal upon command. In the UK, repeaters such as these are normally formally planned and specially licensed by the DTI, and they are often situated in remote sites chosen to give good coverage of an intended service area, to be used by all amateurs as a provided 'service'.

Because of this, repeaters are normally placed in operation by groups of amateurs formed into a 'Repeater Group' for their locality, and they bear the costs of equipment, site rent, electricity, maintenance and so on. The RSGB acts as the coordination body for licensing these in the UK, the appendix at the rear of this book giving details of 2 m and 70 cm repeaters in operation or planned at the time of writing. If your area is not suitably covered, your group could be thinking of placing a unit in operation, hence this short chapter gives a few details on the importance of selecting the correct system, and how to get the RF side in operation either for the main repeater or for a low-cost standby unit to be placed in operation should the main unit fail. Custom-built logic circuitry is normally used to control the repeater, its type and construction being dependant upon the user group's requirements, but this of course is beyond the scope of this book.

High Performance

To achieve simultaneous transmit and receive operation, albeit on differing frequencies, the receiver must have sufficient rejection of strong off-frequency signals, also the transmitter must be spectrally 'clean' without generating spurious signals of high RF noise levels on the co-sited receiver frequency. There must also be adequate aerial isolation between the transmitter and receiver coax feeds, especially if single-aerial use is employed. Let's take a look at each of these in turn:

Receiver Dynamic Range

All receivers are non-linear to some degree, it is the extent of this dynamic range that is important. When receiving a signal on the desired frequency, a *spectrally clean* off-channel signal can 'de-sensitise' the receiver if it causes the active stages to enter into a non-linear state, here the receiver sensitivity effectively becomes progressively worse as the strength of the off-frequency signal increases – this effect is known as 'blocking'. Careful design can improve this, also the use of adequate filtering in the RF and IF stages is of paramount importance. A further problem is that of odd-order intermodulation, i.e. 3rd order and 5th order IMD. Taking an example in the case of 3rd order, off-frequency signals separated by equal amounts of frequency offset may mix together in the receiver to cause a third unwanted product, i.e. 145.550 and 145.350 mixing to generate 145.150. The internally-generated signal here will have the modulation of both off-channel signals superimposed, one at the transmitted deviation and one at twice this deviation, this effect is hence easily identified.

To reduce the effect of the susceptibility to off-frequency signals, filtering improvements need to be made if the receiver active stages are to remain unchanged. 'Close-in' signal rejection, i.e. +/– 25 kHz or so may be improved by a narrower crystal filter being used, if your base station was manufactured for 50 kHz (N) channel spacing it will be fitted with filtering suitable for +/– 15 kHz bandwidth, the answer of course being to retrospectively fit the correct bandwidth of filter, these being available from suppliers such as those listed in the Appendix.

The effect that is the most prevalent however, is that of insufficient rejection of signals spaced by 600 kHz on 2 m, or 1.6 MHz on 70 cm, as encountered from the associated transmitter in an amateur repeater station. Here the use of high-Q cavity filters is normally required, these being electrically resonant and mechanically tunable within the frequency confines of the amateur band. A filter in 'bandpass' mode placed in the coax feed to the receiver aerial connection is always good practice in every amateur repeater, to provide rejection both of other signals in the band and, possibly more importantly, those of transmitters in other parts of the VHF or UHF spectrum on communal radio sites, where several radio users share the same location or even the same aerial mast.

A further refinement is another cavity again in the receiver coax feed, but in this case used in 'notch' configuration tuned to reject the offending transmitter frequency, this normally being the closed-spaced associated repeater transmitter. When used in this manner, a given filter will often provide a greater degree of rejection than that of a bandpass filter, i.e. 30 dB as opposed to 20 dB, but *only* at the tuned frequency. This arrangement may be used where a site is not shared with other users, or alternatively in combination with a bandpass filter to provide a further degree of protection.

The construction of suitable cavity filters is well documented in publications such as the annual ARRL 'Radio Handbook' available from the RSGB. Alternatively you may find suitable filters offered on the surplus market. The UHF AE450F filters found on the surplus market will tune to the 70 cm band adequately, however, suitable VHF filters are fairly rare and often types covering 165–174 MHz will require modification. A useful modification in this case is that of a round metal plate, preferably silver plated, soldered to the bottom of the internal tuning rod to act as a capacitor to the cavity base, effectively lowering the resonant frequency range.

Transmitter Noise

All transmitters generate spurious signals as well as the intended carrier frequency. As well as discrete frequencies such as harmonics of both the carrier and that of the oscillator crystal frequency, a transmitter generates some degree of wideband noise. This noise generally reduces as the frequency difference from the carrier is increased, however it is still present and in an amateur repeater station may indeed cause the effect of de-sensitisation due to transmitted noise present on the associated receiver frequency. It is most important to note that *no* filtering at the receiver can remove this. Again, the use of a cavity filter in bandpass mode is good engineering practice in repeater sites; as well as reducing the level of noise at the receiver frequency it acts as a high-Q filter to reduce the levels of crystal multiples and harmonics of the carrier frequency which may cause interference to other services of more importance than hobbyists such as ourselves. As repeaters are often situated on a site with coverage of a wide population, either on VHF covering an 'area', or on UHF covering a 'community', this often being a large town or city, it is important to ensure the transmitted repeater signal is 'whiter than white'.

Again, in cases where inadequate rejection of the unwanted signal frequency is obtained by the use of a bandpass filter, a further cavity may be used in 'notch' mode in the transmitter coax feed, the notch tuned to the receiver frequency to reduce the level of noise at this frequency.

Aerial Isolation

Because of the above effects, it can be seen that a degree of isolation is required between the transmitter and receiver for the repeater to operate satisfactorily. Let's take the case of a 2 m repeater, with typical levels of transmitter noise at –100 dBc at 600 kHz, and a receiver blocking level of 90 dB again at 600 kHz. If the transmitter is running 20 W, converting this to dBm gives a level of + 43 dBm transmitted power (0 dBm = 1 mW). Hence the transmitter noise at the receiver frequency will be +43 dBm – 100 dB (TX noise level) = –57 dBm. If our receiver threshold, i.e. the minimum detectable signal, is –125 dBm, then we see that a further –57 dBm – (–125 dBm) = 68 dB is required *at the RX frequency*, i.e. in line with the transmitter. Likewise taking receiver blocking into consideration, 43 dBm – 90 dB (RX blocking level) = –47 dBm. Again taking a threshold level of –125 dBm we see that an isolation of –47 dBm – (–125 dBm) = 78 dB is required *at the TX frequency*, i.e. in line with the receiver.

Note however that in normal usage, some degree of aerial isolation is given. Taking the case of separate vertical dipoles mounted above each other, typical isolations given are:

Vertical Separation	145 MHz Isolation	435 MHz Isolation
5 feet	28 dB	50 dB
10 feet	40 dB	62 dB
20 feet	53 dB	73 dB
30 feet	59 dB	—
40 feet	66 dB	—
50 feet	68 dB	—

Here we can see that with suitable aerial separation, and a single bandpass cavity the coax feed to both transmitter and receiver to

A typical repeater with cavity filters, complete with the proud owner.

The AE450F UHF cavity filter.

provide at least 15–20 dB rejection, adequate performance should be obtained unless other forms of 'hop-over' occur. Remember to allow for slight changes in temperature and so on which will reduce the isolation with time, periodic readjustment will sometimes be necessary as a result.

In the case of single aerial operation, using a ferrite circulator, assume an isolation of 20–25 dB *maximum* in the circulator. When a device such as this is used with tuned ports, it is often quite possible to obtain greater isolation by careful tuning, but *be warned*, temperature effects can cause the tuning of these to drift extensively with seasonal and even daily weather variations in remotely sited installations, as well as heating effects from the transmitter PA heatsink.

Equipment Isolation

All the above is of course of little use if direct hop-over occurs, which may be directly between the transmitter and receiver circuitry, or between coax feed lines. The use of well-screened coax is hence required, and the Andrews LDF type of Heliax is recommended due to its low loss and its solid copper outer screen. For interconnections between equipment and cavities, flexible double screened coax is available and is recommended for this.

Where separate TX and RX units are used, e.g. in separate 19 in. rack mounted units with fitted top and bottom screening lids, few problems should result due to circuitry hop-over. By mounting the units physically separated from each other, with the repeater logic control and power supplies in between, further isolation can be achieved.

If however you intend using a base station such as the MF5U with its TX and RX units adjacent to each other in the same cabinet, you may run into problems due to direct transmitter hop-over. In practice a perfect cure has been found by totally enclosing one of the boards, either the TX or the RX, in a suitable die-cast aluminium box housed in the cabinet, with the input and output leads apart from the aerial connection decoupled using 1000pF feed-through capacitors.

In the case of the W15U Westminster, you will normally find adequate isolation exists in the equipment due to the TX and RX circuitry being constructed on separate sides of the centrally-screened chassis. No further internal isolation is hence required, just the normal aerial and cavity isolation external to the unit.

8   ADD-ONS

TRANSCEIVER ACCESSORIES

Fitting a Toneburst

The most common addition to sets for use on 2 m and 70 cm FM is that of a 1750 Hz toneburst. This is to allow UK repeaters to be activated into talkthrough mode, generally a half-second 'bleep' is sufficient, although sometimes this needs to be accompanied by a few seconds of speech for the repeater's logic to 'latch'. Once the repeater has been activated, no further tonebursts are required until the repeater carrier drops again.

There are many toneburst circuits around that are suitable for fitting into a rig, but a few years ago I knocked up a simple circuit that has proved popular with many local amateurs; no doubt someone else out there has done similar. It is about the only circuit I have found that will perform well in sets such as a PF5UH without suffering from RF instability, due to the proximity of transmitted RF power. An 'automatic' toneburst, i.e. one that gives a burst at the beginning of each transmission, has deliberately *not* been described, as these are invariably forgotten and left on by users following initial access, causing subsequent annoyance all round. In the early days of repeaters, this facility was required to reset the access timer, but this is no longer a requirement on any UK repeater conforming to the agreed standards.

Circuit Description

The ceramic resonator is used in conjunction with the inverter gate present in the 4060 IC to form an oscillator, the 1M resistor providing the required amount of voltage feedback to sustain this

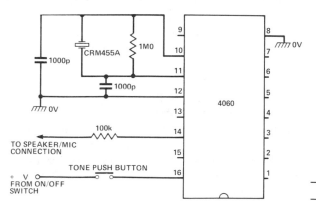

1750Hz toneburst.

oscillation. It deliberately oscillates at slightly lower than 455 kHz due to the two 1000 pF capacitors to ground, to enable it to be divided to 1750 Hz in the 4060 IC, appearing as a square wave at pin 14. Due to this waveform having components only at odd harmonics, it is nicely converted to a sine wave by the transmit audio filtering circuits in the transceiver. In practice you will not need to adjust the frequency of the oscillator to place it on 1750 Hz, as with some other circuits, due to the accurate resonator frequency.

Construction

This circuit is ideal for use where space is limited, due to its low number of components and hence small assembled size. With care in construction, by soldering components directly to the legs of the IC, it may be fitted into many very small places in sets such as the PF5 and PF1 as well as other Pocketphones and into mobile microphone shells. For fitting to mobile equipment itself where space is not at a premium, a small piece of copper strip board such as Veroboard may be used. The resistor and capacitor tolerances are not critical, and any values of within +/-25% of those stated may be used to allow 'junk box' type construction. Be careful when handling the IC as it is a CMOS device, ensuring you do not subject it to high levels of static charge.

The CRM455A type resonator is available from component suppliers such as Cirkit, the remainder of the components from any good electronics retailer.

Connections

You may take power to the toneburst from a suitable push button linked to any supply rail ranging from 5 V to 15 V, with the 0 V connection taken to a common zero voltage rail, this should also be the audio ground. Feed the toneburst audio output to the microphone or speaker/microphone directly, through the 100 K resistor. This resistor value should be satisfactory in virtually all applications, but if for some reason you find the toneburst deviation level requires altering, then decreasing this resistor value will increase the level, increasing the value will decrease the level.

When using this in a mobile equipment, I have often found it very handy to build the circuit into the microphone shell, with a small push-button to activate the tone fitted to the top of the microphone. This is possible with the Europa and Olympic sets, where 10 V is available on the PTT line (mic pins 3 and 5) to power the circuit. Hence, you don't need to fumble around under the dashboard of the car trying to find the toneburst button each time; having the control already in your hand as you are ready to put a call out is a useful safety feature when driving.

TRANSMISSION TIMER

When transmitting either whilst on the move or at home, one must remember the automatic 'Time-Out' period enforced on many repeaters, built in to prevent over-long transmission periods, and hence allow other stations to call in without too long a wait. This time period is often around the two minute mark, and if you go over this limit the repeater will often cut your audio off from its relay path, replacing this with a series of 'engaged' bleeps, alternatively it may well just drop its transmitted carrier and sit there until the input frequency is clear. In either case, no-one else can use the repeater until you have finished. A transmission timer is useful here.

Alternatively, if you dislike one-handed driving for example, you may wish to replace your hand-held microphone with one of the many alternative hands-free microphones. This requires you to use a separate latching toggle switch for transmit/receive change-over. A transmission timer is essential to the socially conscious amateur when using one of these, to prevent long accidental transmissions due to inadvertent operation of the PTT switch.

Circuitry

Several timer circuits have been devised, these often lighting LEDs or sounding bleepers, but they all have the disadvantage of requiring you to switch them on before use, and generally having a high circuit complexity. I have devised a simple timer circuit using

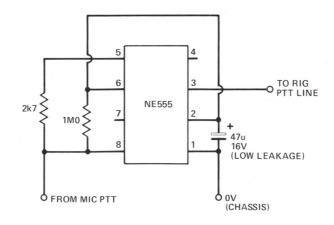

NOTE:
BY USING A 1M PRESET IN PLACE OF THE 1M RESISTOR, VARIABLE TIME LENGTH UP TO TWO MINUTES CAN BE SET. SIMILARLY, USING A 100u CAPACITOR IN PLACE OF THE 47u ONE WILL GIVE YOU UP TO FOUR MINUTES LENGTH.

Transmission timer circuit.

Additions for use with negative transmit keying.

only four components, consisting of two resistors, one capacitor, and the widely available 555 timer IC. Wired into the PTT switching line, this limits your transmission time as required, automatically de-keying your transmitter at the end of the pre-set period.

Being so simple, the components may easily be soldered onto the IC pins, and the entire arrangement placed inside the microphone shell. It operates from a positive PTT switching voltage from 6 V to 13.8 V, meaning that it may be used without modification with the Europa and Olympic series of mobile transceivers, wired in series with the PTT switch linking microphone pins 3 and 5. For use with older equipments such as the Westminster, which use a negative switching line, an extra relay and transistor switch as shown may be added.

If you wish to add a switch to disable the timer for some reason, e.g. for a long simplex chat, a switch applying a short across the capacitor will provide this function.

The values shown in the diagram will provide a time period of just less than two minutes, ideal for repeaters with a two minute time-out period for instance. Increasing the value of the 47 uF capacitor and/or the 1 M resistor will provide a corresponding longer time period if needed. I have added the 2k7 resistor to increase the voltage switching level that is preset internally in the IC, and hence to allow the timing R/C components to be suitable values, hence I would not recommend this resistor value be changed.

2 m/70 cm Aerial Diplexer

When operating on both 2 m and 70 cm bands with your mobile rigs, you may find your car becoming more likened to a porcupine due to the number of mobile whip aerials present. To reduce this number, you may use one of the many types of dual-band whips available, these operate on both 2 m and 70 cm and hence may be used for either band. By using a coax change-over switch, the single aerial may be switched between your 2 m and 70 cm transceivers, alternatively by using a suitable diplexer, simultaneous operation is possible. I designed the following low-cost diplexer many years ago, it has since been built with success by many amateurs throughout the country. It may be easily built from 'junk box' parts, the final

G4HCL 2m/70cm diplexer circuit arrangement.

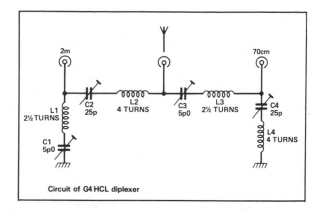

Circuit of G4 HCL diplexer

alignment stages removing the need to use precise values of components as long as those used approximate the required types.

G4HCL Diplexer – Construction

Four good quality trimmer capacitors are required, two of approximately 5pF maximum capacitance and two of approximately 25pF maximum capacitance, together with a length of 1.6mm diameter copper wire, silver plated if possible but not essential, a box and connectors.

A tuned pass circuit resonant on 2 m, consisting of C2 and L2, is used between the aerial port and the 2 m port. Likewise a 70 cm pass circuit comprising of C3 and L3 is used between the aerial port and the 70 cm port. Between the 2 m port and ground, a similar 70 cm pass circuit consisting of C1 and L1 is used to conduct any 70 cm RF to ground, similarly a 2 m pass circuit consisting of C4 and L4 is used between the 70 cm port and ground.

It is built in a screened box, an Eddystone die-cast type of 1 in × 1 in. × 3 in. being ideal. Three coaxial sockets are used, for the aerial, 70 cm, and 2 m ports, these should be of as low loss as possible, i.e. BNC or N-type rather than SO-239. Place the 2 m and 70 cm connectors on either side of the aerial connector rather than next to each other, giving maximum isolation. All coils are wound on a ¼ in. former – a drill bit may be used for this, with wire diameter spacing between turns. The best trimmers to use are the multi-turn variety, but any mechanically stable types will suffice adequately. Construct the circuit by soldering directly to the capacitor and coax socket pins to keep lead lengths as short as possible, and use solder tags screwed to the socket fixing holes for ground connections.

Alignment

1. Connect your 2 m and 70 cm transceivers to their relevant ports,

do *not* transmit at this stage. Tune to a reasonably weak 2 m signal and tune C2 for the best received signal strength. Now transfer to the 70 cm transceiver, and tune C3 for best reception of a received 70 cm signal.

2. Now reverse the aerial connections, i.e. connect the 2 m port to the 70 cm transceiver and the 70 cm port to the 2 m transceiver. Once again, do *not* transmit yet. Tune to a fairly strong 2 m signal, and adjust C4 for *minimum* received signal strength. Then tune to a fairly strong 70 cm signal, and tune C1 again for minimum signal strength.

3. Now revert back to the original connections, with the 2 m and 70 cm transceivers connected to their respective aerial ports. It is now safe to transmit. Final trimming may be performed by placing a power meter in the aerial line, i.e. between the diplexer and aerial or 50 ohm load, and slightly adjusting C2 for maximum power with the 2 m transmitter keyed, and C3 for maximum with the 70 cm keyed. This final operation should ensure 'spot on' performance.

During each of the above alignment stages, ensure that the proximity of the lid does not affect the tuning adjustments made, a slight retune being undertaken as necessary if this does occur. When correctly built and aligned, the diplexer will typically achieve over 70 dB isolation between 2 m and 70 cm ports, with less than 0.2 dB loss in each 'leg'.

RECEIVER PREAMPLIFIERS

Some amateurs who convert sets for fringe coverage use when mobile, for instance at the limit of range of 2 m repeaters, may find further receiver sensitivity of use, particularly if an add-on amplifier such as the A200 is used to boost the transmit power even further. These are available as ready-assembled units or as user-assembled kits. Due to the RF nature of preamplifier circuitry with its high gain and stability criteria, I would not recommend trying to build one from scratch using your own PCB etc. as you are likely to end up very disappointed. It is important for example to use the correct *type* of PCB, capacitors, resistors etc. as well as the correct values of these. The use of preamp modules, i.e. the bare electronics without any cases or interconnections, can hence reap rewards.

I have picked out a few such preamp modules, which apart from low cost and reasonable performance have the benefit of a very small size combined with low current drain. This will enable it to be physically placed in circuit inside mobile sets as well as the PF2 and PF3 series of portables. I have also found that by placing one line with the 'straight through' switched path of an A200, the arrangement acts as a very useful add-on to improve communication range on both transmit and receive.

2 m/70 cm Preamplifier Kits

If you are skilled in RF construction techniques, you may care to note that a pair of small preamplifier kits are available from Cirkit in the UK (address and phone no. in the Appendix). These are available for the 2 m band, stock No. 41-01307 (at around £6) and for the 70 cm band stock No. 41-01506 (at around £7). The 2 m preamp is 34 mm × 9 mm × 15 mm, operating from an 8–16 V supply, the 70 cm preamp is 50 mm × 10 mm × 17 mm, operating from an 8–12 V supply. Following construction, make very sure you have checked for the absence of unwanted solder links between adjacent tracks; due to the proximity of these, even skilled constructors have problems!

Place the unit into circuit, remembering to place this in the receive path only, i.e. the coax or PCB track between the receiver aerial input and the TX/RX aerial changeover switch. On receiving a very weak off-air signal, tune both ferrite cores on the 2 m unit with a non-metallic adjuster for best receive signal, likewise on the 70 cm preamp, but here you only need to tune the variable capacitor, as the two small helical resonators are pre-aligned.

Ready-Built 2 m/4 m/6 m Preamplifier

Garex Ltd in the UK, apart from being a useful source of surplus equipment, supply a suitable VHF preamp at reasonable cost for those not wishing to or not being able to assemble such a circuit. The unit is available at just over the £10 mark at the time of writing, and comes in 6 m, 4 m, and 2 m versions, all these having the same

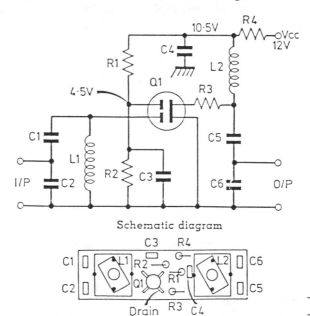

Schematic diagram

Garex Preamplifier.

size and circuit configuration but with differing component and inductor values.

Circuit Description

The capacitive tap on the inductor L1 matches the 50 ohm input to gate 1 of the MOSFET, this being a BF981 with a low claimed noise figure of the order of 1 dB. C1 and C2 values are further optimised to achieve minimum overall noise figure for the circuit, hence giving the best achievable sensitivity. The capacitively tapped output network resonates the output in the centre at the desired operating frequency range. R3 is a parasitic oscillation suppressor, and combined with the careful PCB layout, prevents UHF oscillation of the BF981. The unit measures 34 mm × 9 mm × 15 mm and draws 5–10 mA from an 8–17 V supply.

REPLACEMENT UHF HELICAL AERIAL

When using sets such as the PF5UH, PF1 or similar, you may find their internal aerial to be adequate for many needs, but may occasionally wish for better performance. Alternatively, you may wish to add an external BNC aerial co-axial connector to allow you to connect an external mobile whip or roof-top aerial for home use. In either case, a replacement compact aerial of good performance is required for fitting to the set top.

Rather than purchase a commercial portable whip or helical fitted with a suitable BNC base, I have found my portable helical design

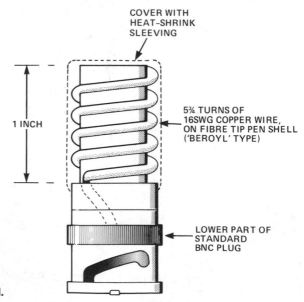

COVER WITH
HEAT-SHRINK
SLEEVING

1 INCH

5¾ TURNS OF
16SWG COPPER WIRE,
ON FIBRE TIP PEN SHELL
('BEROYL' TYPE)

LOWER PART OF
STANDARD
BNC PLUG

High performance compact UHF helical.

shown here to have good performance. In a test using accurate laboratory equipment, when mounted on a Yaesu FT708R UHF portable, it was found to out-perform the supplied 1/4 wave whip by just over 0.5 dB. Excellent results are also given on the PF5UH and PF2UH, and these aerials are in use by several amateurs in my locality.

Construction

The bottom section of a BNC plug shell is used for the body of the helical base, into this a plastic fibre tip pen shell is fitted and made ready to be secured. I have found the commonly available 'Beroyl' pen cases to provide a secure fit without the need for additional adhesive. Wind five and three quarter turns of 16 gauge copper wire around this, spreading the turns so the length of the resultant coil is exactly 1 in. Insert the 'tail' of the coil through a small hole made in the plastic shell, and solder this end to the BNC centre pin, you will find this removes from the plug very easily. Reassemble the shell into the plug body, cover it with heat shrink sleeving to provide a weatherproof finish, and away you go.

9   INSTALLATION ADVICE

Mobile Installation

Here we deal with the installation and positioning of mobile equipment, and its use with a view to maximum road safety. We have previously seen the advantages of a remote mount set, with its small control box linked to the main transceiver placed under the seat or in a car boot. The remote set itself normally fits in a metal cradle, but ensure that you do not drill into items such as a petrol tank when remote mounting. I know it sounds like common sense but you'd be surprised how many amateurs don't know that the tank itself is often positioned at the rear of the car, with its metalwork easily accessible.

Dash Mounts

Remember that many car dashboards are now made of plastic, and sometimes cannot support the weight of an early (hence fairly large and heavy) model of transceiver. One form of mounting I have seen used a number of times is that of placing the set vertically between the passenger and driver seats with the controls pointing upwards towards the driver, the case secured to the vehicle's central column. This is not the most ideal position of course, but it may be better than restricting the control of the car through insufficient leg room for pedal movement, or placing the set on the passenger side of the dashboard hence requiring a large stretch to operate it.

If you have the matching mobile bracket with your set, by all means use this for securing the set. Make use of the existing mounting holes in this bracket as a template for drilling, this can save many measuring mistakes. If this method cannot be used for some reason, or you have made up your own mobile mounting bracket, remember the adage 'measure twice, drill once', it can save a lot of heartache as well as unwanted holes in your car. Ensure that no electrical cables run behind your intended drilling position, these wrap themselves around a drill bit very quickly and can easily start a fire in your vehicle.

DC Connections

When connecting the set to the vehicle supply, you will find it electrically better to wire it to the vehicle battery contacts themselves rather than to an 'accessory' supply, especially in the case of high power sets. Amplifiers such as A200s often draw such a level of current as to make this direct wiring a necessary requirement. Ensure you add suitable fuses in line with the supply leads, placed as close to the battery connections as possible, to allow a degree of protection from fire. Car accessory shops stock simple clip-on holders to match standard car fuses. These are widely available, and being very cheap and easy to install there is really no excuse for omitting them. Where the supply leads pass through the bulkhead, ensure they are protected from chafing by using a rubber or plastic grommet to save problems in the months to come. You may find the use of an accessory supply handy though because it automatically removes DC voltage when you switch the ignition off, this saves you leaving the set switched on accidentally when out of the car and hence possibly flattening your battery. You may of course use this accessory supply to energize the coil of a heavy-duty DC relay, with its contacts in series with the lead from your direct battery to the radios, hence giving the best of both worlds.

OPERATION ON THE MOVE

When dash mounting, attempt as far as possible to place the set so that minimum eye travel distance occurs between the set and the road ahead, to enable you to quickly see the channel you are operating on, and to locate the positions of the volume and squelch knobs for operation. The ideal position is on top of the dashboard, if this can be done without obscuring the view of the road ahead or other vehicle controls. If not, make sure the set is positioned in a place where it will not restrict your ability to control the car, also in the case of an accident, where it would not hinder you from escaping from the vehicle (I never thought this could happen to me either until I climbed out of an overturned car).

If you cannot place the set in an 'ideal' position, do ensure it is placed where all the controls are within easy reach, so that you can operate the set without shifting from your normal seated position. Stretching over to reach to the other end of the car to change channel is a short cut to an early grave. If the set is not in immediate view when driving, don't be tempted to look at it to operate, but get used to checking or changing the channel, for instance by counting the number of 'clicks' from the channel 1 'stop' position – learn to use it by 'feel' alone.

Microphones
Make sure your microphone hanger is placed in such a position so that when the microphone is in place its lead does not interfere with the vehicle's controls, likewise when in use ensure it does not cut across the steering wheel for instance. A careful bit of planning

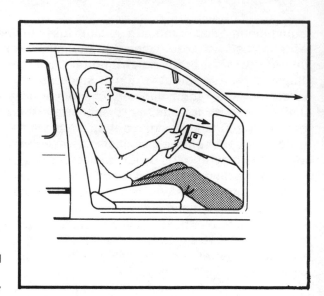

Minimum eye travel distance required to operate controls.

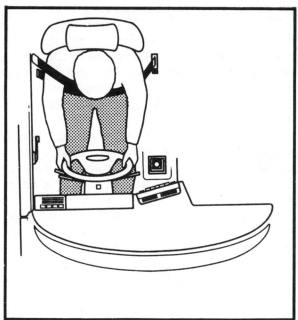

All controls within easy reach.

again before drilling the hole brings many benefits!

The Highway Code at the time of writing recommends you not to use a hand held microphone whilst on the move, the Highway Code is *not* the law but this could be a sensible precaution in some instances. If you prefer, there are several makes of gooseneck and neck slung microphones which are available from commercial amateur equipment dealers. These must be used in combination with a separate transmit/receive switch for PTT operation. If you use a toggle switch for this, *do* ensure that the microphone switching circuit has a time-out timer fitted. If not, fit one! A suitable circuit using a minimum of components is shown in the previous chapter. This will ensure you do not accidentally drive around with your transmitter constantly keyed, transmitting through your local repeater while all the other users are alternately cursing you or listening to you cursing other traffic. Yes, I've heard this happen several times due to the use of these. The dangers of this occurring during something like a Raynet operation on their dedicated emergency channel defy description.

MOBILE AERIALS

All radio equipment needs an aerial to operate of course. For 2 m, 4 m and 70 cm mobile use this normally takes the form of a short whip fitted to a suitable base mounted on the car metalwork. In the past, the general feeling was to drill a hole 'slap bang' in the middle of the roof for this, being the most ideal position for it electrically. Aesthetically, this however may not be suitable as many car owners may realise, also drivers of leased vehicles may be prohibited from drilling holes into the car metalwork. Having been 'through' several cars myself, with no holes drilled but still having transceivers installed for 10 m, 4 m, 2 m and 70 cm as well as business radio, cellular, and my normal broadcast radio, it took a bit of thinking! The following may give you some insight to the types of mounts, aerials, and their positioning. It is by no means exhaustive but it may give you a few ideas.

Aerial Types

4 m (70 MHz) 4 m aerials used in a mobile environment are usually a standard quarter wave due to ther length, and literally any form of straight metal rod will do here. As an alternative to your broadcast aerial, you may wish to fit a stainless steel 4 m quarter wave in its place, with coax fed to a relay inside the car to switch between your 4 m transceiver or connection to the car radio. If so, I would suggest placing a trimmer capacitor across the feed to the car radio, adjusting this for maximum received strength on a weak MW signal. This is because the coax feed to a normal car radio aerial has additional capacitance present, which of course is absent when we replace it with 50 ohm coax. In the past, I have used this arrangement coupled to my 4 m Reporter, using the auxiliary power switching leads present on this to switch the relay coil. Because 4 m is generally a 'UK' only band, you may sometimes find imported amateur aerials for this difficult to obtain, however Revco and Jaybeam manufacture a suitable range.

2 m (145 MHz) Being the most popular VHF amateur band across the world, a large variety of whip aerials are available. The Japanese versions invariably have a PL259 type screw-on base to suit a matching SO239 car aerial mount, this makes removal or replacement fairly easy but offer easy picking for a thief. With some aerials costing up to £50, a spot of epoxy resin would not go amiss here unless you methodically remove the aerial every time you leave the vehicle.

As well as the standard quarter wave whip, this being around 19 ins. long, several forms of 'gain' aerial whips are available, such as a 1/2 wave, 5/8th, 6/8th, 7/8th and so on, the 7/8th being very popular. Vertically placed gain aerials operate by compressing the radiated power in the horizontal plane, with maximum radiation towards the horizon. Remember that when you drive at speed, a long aerial such as the 7/8th does bend substantially with the resultant radiation going up in the air in front of the car, and down into the ground behind it, hence these types do have disadvantages as well as advantages. From many controlled mobile aerial tests, I have always found the best compromise to be a relatively short aerial such as a 1/2 wave on 2 m.

70 cm (435 MHz) Again on this band there are a wide variety of gain whips available, and due to the short length of a quarter wave on this band (6 ins.) it can often make sense to use a gain type unless you mainly operate in built-up areas. These are usually made up from 1/4 wave and 5/8th wave sections, with either moulded or open-wound phasing coils in series with the vertical whip sections.

Because UHF communication in built-up areas is often achieved by reflection from buildings, a very high gain aerial with little radiation at high angles can be a positive disadvantage here. However if the majority of your driving is done in rural areas, a high gain aerial that does not bend excessively at speed may prove beneficial. A useful compromise is a 5/8th over 5/8th whip.

Dual Band Aerials (145/435 MHz) As more amateurs are finding that 2 m and 70 cm both have their own advantages, 2 m for wide area communication and 70 cm for 'community' repeater use, dual band whips are finding favour amongst many amateurs. The usual type, which is widely available from several manufacturers, is the 3 ft long variety acting as a loaded 1/2 wave or 5/8th on 2 m, and a 5/8th on 70 cm. Other types are of course available, longer ones offering higher gain at low driving speeds, and shorter types for uses where the aerial needs to be inconspicuous. I have had good success with the tiny 'Comet' dual band whip mounted at roof level, this being a mere 8 ins. long and which I now use in preference to my 3 ft long variety previously mounted on the rear wing.

To allow use on both bands, a coax switch between the two transceivers must be used, alternatively a diplexer to electrically separate the two frequency bands may be used to allow simultaneous operation of both sets with the one aerial. The latter arrangement is the most popular, as it allows you to listen out on one band while having a chat on the other. These diplexers are widely available commercially, and Chapter 8 gives details of the construction of a low-cost high performance unit.

Mounts

As well as drilling a hole in the metalwork to affix a suitable aerial whip mount, various types of 'no-hole' fixings are available.

The Gutter Mount This screws to the small rain gutter running along either side of the car roof from front to rear. Before going out and buying such a mount, ensure your car does actually have a gutter (some don't), and if so make sure it is metal. Often plastic gutters are fitted, which apart from possibly being too weak to survive an aerial impact with a tree or large bird, will not provide the necessary ground plane connection many aerials such as the 1/4 wave require. The aerial coax is run along to enter the car normally past a door rubber seal, so ensure this coax isn't positioned where water ingress can occur.

Boot Mount This clips to the side of the rear boot lip, the coax passing through the gap between the boot lip and the car body. Make sure you have enough clearance here, otherwise you'll soon find the plastic coax outer cover becomes worn and water enters the coax braid, capillary action quickly rendering the coax useless. Hatchback vehicles may often make use of such a mount when clipped to the top of the hatchback lid, on the metal portion above the rear window. If so, ensure that when the hatchback is opened, the resultant angle doesn't cause damage to the car roof from the mount or the aerial.

Magnetic Mounts These have advantages for use as a temporary fixture, for example when regularly driving different cars or for use in areas where vandalism is prevalent. The mount may be quickly fitted and removed, however when placing it in position, ensure no small particles of grit are present that could damage the paintwork, ___ likewise when removing the mount, pull it off vertically, *never* slide it off if you value your paintwork. The coax feed normally passes through a window or past a rubber door seal, again ensure this will not suffer water ingress when driving, you'd be surprised how much water can flow along such a coax installation when driving through a rainstorm! Due to wind-loading effects, I would advise against using long high-gain aerials with these mounts. A cautionary note also is that mag-mounts can instantly render the rear magnetic strips on credit cards useless, so beware!

On-Glass Mounts These have become popular lately from their widespread use on 900 MHz cellular installations. Types with suitable interior matching units are now available for 70 cm and are becoming available for 2 m, from UK manufacturers such as APL and Panorama. Their prices however are not cheap, (around £50) and only low-gain aerials may be used due to physical considerations, hence their use could be limited for some amateurs. For use on a new or company 'fleet' car, where aesthetics are important, one of these mounts could be ideal. The aerials and mounts are often coloured matt black, hence making them very inconspicuous.

AERIAL POSITIONING

A simple rule often holds true here, place the aerial as much in the clear as possible, but with as much metalwork below it as possible. If the aerial is positioned adjacent to a metal pillar, this will detune the aerial as well as inhibit radiation in that direction, so keep it as far away as possible. Likewise, never consider mounting the aerial on a bumper to reduce overall height, with the lower part of its whip right next to the car's metalwork. In this case, it would often be far better using a shorter aerial placed on the wing or gutter.

Ground Plane
Remember that many aerials need a metal 'ground plane' to operate, this is formed by the car body. When using a magnetic mount, the circular base forms a capacitor coupling to the metalwork providing a degree of ground plane. When using other forms of mount such as a gutter or boot mount, ensure the fixing screws penetrate the paintwork and connect to the metalwork. Don't be tempted to use rubber pads or whatever on these screws to protect the car paintwork. If the aerial needs a ground plane which you don't provide you're wasting your time, so use a different type of mount instead. If you cannot supply a ground plane, for instance if your vehicle has a fibreglass body, various types of helical ground

'counterpoises' are available from UK manufacturers which fit to the lower section of the mount.

Tilt-Over

The aerial *must* be mounted vertically to operate correctly, especially so in the case of gain aerials. It may look 'smart' to have it tilted back in a 'streamlined' fashion but it won't work very well, so use a shorter aerial mounted vertically if you need to reduce the overall height in use. If you regularly garage your car, or use multi-storey car parks, some aerial bases are provided with a 'tilt-over' facility where following an upward pull, you may place the aerial horizontally along your car roof. These may be used with a gutter mount next to the driver's window, so while you're queuing for the car park you can quickly put your arm out and tilt the aerial. Other forms have a large wing-nut on the mount to allow quick tilting or removal. If you need to reduce the overall height of your aerial but only for instances such as these, the use of a tilt-over mount on the gutter could be preferable to a boot mount in terms of achieving better performance.

ELECTRICAL NOISE SUPPRESSION

All cars are invariably fitted with some form of electric circuitry, even in the case of diesel cars where ignition interference has become a thing of the past. Vehicle manufacturers now often go to great lengths to reduce interference, especially with the popularity of FM car radios, these now often being fitted as standard. However older vehicles do sometimes emit RF noise that could prove troublesome at the lower frequencies such as 4 m and 2 m.

Ignition Noise

Normally the worst offenders in the ignition system are the sparks generated in the plugs, these being coupled to nice aerials called ignition leads. The latter are often suppressed themselves, but some enthusiastically 'tuned' cars have been fitted with copper leads; this is worthwhile checking. Plug-on resistive or inductive suppressors are available (such as Lucas type LS632 VHF suppressors) which may be fitted in a matter of seconds. The distributor is often a further source of radiation, and again a plug-on suppressor may be used on the HT lead, but in stubborn cases, a screening can may be used over the distributor cap.

A further useful measure is to 'bond' the car bonnet to the car body at the hinge positions, using short lengths of thick copper braid. Following the ignition systems, small electrical motors cause a large

LUCAS SUPPRESSION EQUIPMENT

LS No.	Part No.	Description	LS No.	Part No.	Description
LS627	60600385	1 µF Capacitor with connector, for Ignition	LS642	60670350	General Purpose Bonding Strap.
LS628	60600386	1 µF Capacitor with connector, for Generator	LS646	60460665	Inline Resistor for Wire HT Cables
LS629	54200297	3 µF Capacitor for internal mounting on 15–16–17–18 ACR Alternators	LS648	60460666	Right Angled Plug Suppressor, with shroud
LS630	60460085	Inline Choke	LS673	54200423	3 µF Capacitor for internal mounting on 23-25 ACR Alternators.
LS631	60046089	Straight VHF Plug Suppressors. Pack of Four	LS674	60410139	Screening Can for 45D4 Distributors
LS632	54421964	Straight VHF Plug Suppressor			
LS633	60046090	Right Angled VHF Plug Suppressors. Pack of Four	LS680	78139	1 µF Capacitor with Dual Connectors
LS634	54422760	Right Angled VHF Plug Suppressor	LS681	78158	Control Box Filter Unit with mounting bracket
LS635	60046091	Straight VHF Distributor Suppressors. Pack of five.			
LS636	54421441	Straight VHF Distributor Suppressor			
LS637	60046092	Right Angled Distributor Suppressors. Pack of Five.	LS682	54201329	3 µF Capacitor for internal mounting on 20 ACR Alternators
LS638	54423567	Right Angled Distributor Suppressor.	LS683	54418559	Screening Can for 23-25D Distributors.
LS639	60150093	7 Amp Inline Choke			
LS640	60150094	3 Amp Inline Choke			
LS641	60670378	7 Amp Choke Assembly for 14-15-16W Wiper Motors.	LS684	60150114	Dynamo Feed through Capacitor

Typical add-on suppression components.

number of problems in use, particularly the windscreen wiper motor. DC chokes placed in series with the leads to these motors may be used, but ensure they are of suitable current handling capability. Plug-in multiple choke assemblies are available for these, such as the Lucas LS641 unit for 14–15–16 W wiper motors.

Alternator Whine

If you find a varying whistle superimposed on your transmitted audio, this sometimes being apparent on received audio also, check if the frequency of this varies in sympathy with the speed of the engine. If so, this is most likely to be alternator whine. I have noticed this to a large degree with Europa transceivers, and you can adjust the internal 'Set 14V' preset potentiometer to provide 12–12.5 V instead to supply the transceiver circuitry rather than limiting at 14 V. This has the effect of chopping the superimposed alternator voltage pulses. With other sets, you will find that placing a DC choke of around 2–3 mH in series with the positive supply lead to the transceiver, followed by an electrolytic capacitor of around 1,000 uF across the supply at the transceiver side, will effect a substantial reduction. Again, ensure the choke is of sufficient current handling capability to withstand the transmit current of the set.

APPENDIX 1 – BAND PLANS

6 m Bandplan

50.000			
:	CW Only	50.020–50.080	Beacons
:		50.090	CW Activity Centre
:			
50.100			
:		50.110	International Calling
:	All Modes	50.100–50.300	SSB DX
:	(narrow band)	50.300	CW Meteor Scatter
:		50.350	SSB Meteor Scatter
50.500			
:	All Modes	50.600–50.700	Packet Radio
51.000			
:	DX Window		
51.100			
:	All Modes	51.410–51.590	FM Channels
52.000		51.510	FM Calling

4 m Bandplan

70.000			
:	Beacons		
70.075			
:	CW Only		
70.150			
:	SSB/CW	70.200	SSB Calling
70.260			
:		70.260	Mobile Calling
:	All Modes	70.300	RTTY Calling
:		70.350–70.400	Raynet
70.400			
:	FM Simplex	70.450	FM Calling
70.500			

2 m Bandplan

144.000		144.000–144.025	Moonbounce
:	CW Only	144.050	CW Calling
:		144.100	Meteor Scatter CW

144.150			
:		144.250	Used for GB2RS News and slow morse
:	SSB/CW	144.260	Used by Raynet
:		144.300	SSB Calling
:	144.400		Meteor Scatter SSB
144.500		144.500	SSTV Calling
:		144.600	RTTY FSK
:		144.625	Digital Modes
:		144.650	Packet Calling/BBS
:	All Modes	144.675	Packet Radio Working
:		144.700	FAX Calling
:		144.750	ATV Calling/ Talkback
:		144.775	Raynet
:		144.800	Raynet
:		144.825	Raynet
144.845			
:	Beacons		
144.990			
:		145.000	R0 Input
:		145.025	R1 Input
:		145.050	R2 Input
:		145.075	R3 Input
:	FM Repeater Inputs	145.100	R4 Input
:		145.125	R5 Input
:		145.150	R6 Input
:		145.175	R7 Input
145.200		145.200	S8 Raynet
:		145.225	S9 Used by Raynet
:		145.250	S10 Used for Slow Morse
:		145.275	S11
:		145.300	S12 RTTY AFSK
:		145.325	S13
:		145.350	S14
:	FM Simplex Channels	145.375	S15
:		145.400	S16
:		145.425	S17
:		145.450	S18
:		145.475	S19
:		145.500	S20 FM Calling

		145.525	S21 Used for GB2RS News
:		145.550	S22 Used for mobile rally talk-in
:		145.575	S23
145.600		145.600	R0 Output
:		145.625	R1 Output
:	FM Repeater	145.650	R2 Output
:	Outputs	145.675	R3 Output
:		145.700	R4 Output
:		145.725	R5 Output
:		145.750	R6 Output
:		145.775	R7 Output
145.800			
:	Satellites		
146.000			

70 cm Bandplan

430.000			
:	Not formally		Note: 431.000–
:	planned		432.000 not available
:			within 100 km of
:			Charing Cross,
:			London.
432.000			
:		432.000–432.025	Moonbounce
:	CW Only	432.050	Centre of CW activity
:			
432.150			
:		432.200	Centre of SSB activity
:	SSB/CW	432.350	Microwave talk-back
:			
432.500			
:		432.600	RTTY Calling
:		432.600+/–	FSK RTTY Working
:	All Modes	432.675	Data Calling
:		432.700	FAX Calling
432.800			
:	Beacons		
433.000		433.000	RB0 Output
:		433.025	RB1 Output
:		433.050	RB2 Output
:		433.075	RB3 Output

:		433.100	RB4 Output
:	FM Repeater	433.125	RB5 Output
:	Outputs	433.150	RB6 Output
:	(UK only)	433.175	RB7 Output
:		433.200	RB8 Output
:		433.225	RB9 Output
:		433.250	RB10 Output
:		433.275	RB11 Output
:		433.300	RB12 Output/RTTY AFSK
:		433.325	RB13 Output
:		433.350	RB14 Output
:		433.375	RB15 Output
433.400		433.400	SU16
:		433.425	SU17
:		433.450	SU18
:		433.475	SU19
:		433.500	SU20 FM Calling
:	FM Simplex	433.525	SU21 Used for mobile rally talk-in
:		433.550	SU22
:		433.575	SU23
:		433.600	SU24 RTTY AFSK
:		433.700	Raynet
:		433.725	Raynet
:	433.750		Raynet
:		433.775	Raynet
434.600		434.600	RB0 Input
:		434.625	RB1 Input
:		434.650	RB2 Input
:		434.675	RB3 Input
:		434.700	RB4 Input
:		434.725	RB5 Input
:		434.750	RB6 Input
:	FM Repeater	434.775	RB7 Input
:	Inputs	434.800	RB8 Input
:		434.825	RB9 Input
:		434.850	RB10 Input
:		434.875	RB11 Input
:		434.900	RB12 Input RTTY Repeater
:		434.925	RB13 Input
:		434.950	RB14 Input
:		434.975	RB15 Input

435.000

:

:

440.000

435.000–438.000 Satellites
434.000–440.000 Fast Scan ATV

APPENDIX 2 – UK REPEATERS

UK 2 m FM Repeaters

R0: 145.000 MHz Input, 145.600 MHz Output

GB3AS	Aldbeck, Cumbria
GB3CF	Leicester
GB3EL	East London
GB3FF	Burntisland, Fife
GB3LY	Limavady, Co. Londonderry
GB3MB	Manchester
GB3SS	Knockmore, Nr. Elgin
GN3WR	Nr. Wells, Somerset

R1: 145.025MHz Input, 145.625MHz Output

GB3GD	Snaefell, Isle of Man
GB3HG	North Yorks
GB3KS	Dover, Kent
GB3MH	Malvern Hills, Worcs
GB3NB	Wymondham, Norfolk
GB3NG	Near Peterhead, Grampian
GB3PA	Paisley, Scotland
GB3SC	Bournemouth, Dorset
GB3SI	St. Ives, Cornwall
GB3WL	Hillingdon, West London

R2: 145.050MHz Input, 145.650MHz Output

GB3AY	Lethanhill, 15km S.E. of Ayr
GB3BX	North Birmingham
GB3GJ	Jersey, Channel Islands
GB3HS	Little Weighton, Humberside
GB3MN	Stockport, Cheshire
GB3OC	Orkney Islands
GB3SB	Duns, Berwickshire
GB3SL	South London
GB3TR	Torquay, Devon
GB3WH	Nr. Swindon

R3: 145.075MHz Input, 145.675MHz Output

GB3BM	Birmingham, West Midlands
GB3DR	Bulbarrow Hill, Dorset

GB3ES	Hastings, East Sussex
GB3LD	Barrow in Furness, Cumbria
GB3LU	Shetland Islands
GB3NA	Barnsley, Yorkshire
GB3PE	Peterborough
GB3PO	Martlesham Heath, Suffolk
GB3PR	Perth, Scotland
GB3RD	10k W. Reading
GB3SA	Swansea, West Glamorgan

R4: 145.100MHz Input, 145.700MHz Output

GB3AR	Arfon, Nr. Caernarfon, Gwynedd
GB3BB	Brecon, Powys
GB3BT	Berwick Upon Tweed
GB3EV	Appleby, Cumbria
GB3HH	Buxton, Derbyshire
GB3HI	Isle of Mull, Scotland
GB3KN	Nr. Maidstone, Kent
GB3VA	16km W. Aylesbury, Bucks
GB3WD	Princedown, Devon

R5: 145.125MHz Input, 145.725MHz Output

GB3BI	Mounteagle, Near Inverness
GB3DA	Danbury, Essex
GB3LM	Lincoln
GB3NC	St. Austell, Cornwall
GB3NI	Belfast, Northern Ireland
GB3SN	Fourmarks, Hampshire
GB3TP	Keighley, West Yorks
GB3TW	Tyne and Wear
GB3VT	Stoke on Trent, Staffs

R6: 145.150 MHz Input, 145.750 MHz Output

GB3AM	Longbridge, S. Birmingham
GB3BC	8km NNW. Newport, Gwent
GB3CS	Blackhill, Central Scotland
GB3MP	Moel-Y-Parc, Clwyd
GB3PI	Barkway, Hertfordshire
GB3TY	Nr. Hexham, Northumberland
GB3WS	Horsham, W. Sussex

R7: 145.175MHz Input, 145.775MHz Output

| GB3FR | Old Bolingbroke, Lincolnshire |

GB3GN   Durris, Near Aberdeen
GB3NL   Enfield, North London
GB3PW   Newtown, Powys
GB3RF   Burnley, Lancashire
GB3SR   Worthing, Sussex
GB3WK   Leamington Spa
GB3WT   West Tyrone, N. Ireland
GB3WW   4km N. Crosshands, Dyfed

70cm Repeaters

RB0: 434.600 MHz Input, 433.000 MHz Output

GB3BN   Bracknell, Berkshire
GB3CK   Charing, Ashford, Kent
GB3DT   Bulbarrow Hill, Dorset
GB3EX   Exeter, Devon
GB3KB   Farnborough, Kent
GB3LL   Llandudno
GB3MK   Milton Keynes, Bucks
GB3MS   Malvern Hills, Worcs
GB3NR   Norwich, Norfolk
GB3NT   Newcastle-Upon-Tyne
GB3NY   Scarborough, North Yorks
GB3PF   Pendle Forest, Blackburn, Lancs
GB3PU   Perth
GB3SO   Boston, Lincs
GB3SV   Bishops Stortford, Herts
GB3US   Sheffield
GB3WN   Wolverhampton

RB1: 434.625MHz Input, 433.025MHz Output

GB3BA   Nr. Aberdeen
GB3BV   Hemel Hempstead, Herts
GB3HO   Horsham, Sussex
GB3MA   Central Manchester

RB2: 434.650MHz Input, 433.050MHz Output

GB3AV   Aylesbury, Bucks
GB3CH   25km West of Plymouth
GB3CI   Corby, Northamptonshire
GB3EK   Margate, Kent
GB3FC   Fylde Coast, Lancashire
GB3HD   Huddersfield, W. Yorks
GB3LS   Lincoln

GB3LV	Enfield, North London
GB3NN	Wells, Norfolk
GB3NX	Crawley, West Sussex
GB3OS	Stourbridge, Worcs.
GB3PH	Portsdown Hill, Hampshire
GB3ST	Stoke on Trent, Staffs
GB3UL	Belfast, N. Ireland
GB3YS	Yeovil, Somerset

RB3: 434.675MHz Input, 433.075MHz Output

GB3HL	Hillingdon, Middlesex
GB3HU	Hull, Humberside
GB3NH	Northampton
GB3VS	Taunton, Somerset

RB4: 434.700MHz Input, 433.100MHz Output

GB3AN	Anglesey
GB3GC	Goole, Humberside
GB3IH	Ipswich, Suffolk
GB3IW	Isle of Wight
GB3KL	Kings Lynn, Norfolk
GB3KM	Knockmore, Nr. Elgin
GB3KR	Kidderminster, Worcs.
GB3LE	Leicester
GB3NK	Wrotham, Kent
GB3OH	Linlithgow, West Lothian
GB3SP	5½km East of Pembroke, Dyfed
GB3UB	Bath, Avon

RB5: 434.725MHz Input, 433.125MHz Output

GB3GH	Gloucester
GB3HY	Haywards Heath, West Sussex
GB3NW	Hendon, London
GB3OV	Huntingdon
GB3WJ	Scunthorpe

RB6: 434.750 MHz Input, 433.150 MHz Output

GB3BD	Bedford
GB3BE	Bury St. Edmunds, Suffolk
GB3BR	Race Hill, Brighton, Sussex
GB3CR	Mold, Clwyd
GB3CW	Newtown, Powys
GB3HA	Hornsea, Humberside

GB3HC	Hereford
GB3LW	Central London
GB3ME	Rugby, Warwickshire
GB3NM	Mapperley, Near Nottingham
GB3SK	Canterbury, Kent
GB3SW	Salisbury
GB3SY	Barnsley, South Yorkshire
GB3WG	Port Talbot, Wales

RB7: 434.775MHz Input, 433.175MHz Output

| GB3DG | Dumfries and Galloway |
| GB3HZ | Nr. High Wycombe, Bucks |

RB8: 434.800MHz Input, 433.200MHz Output

| GB3CM | Carmarthen |
| GB3EH | Edge Hill, Warwickshire |

RB10: 434.850MHz Input, 433.250MHz Output

GB3AW	Ashmansworth, Hampshire
GB3BS	Bristol, Avon
GB3DD	Dundee
GB3DY	Nr. Wirksworth, Derbyshire
GB3ER	Danbury, Essex
GB3LI	Liverpool, Merseyside
GB3LT	Luton, Bedfordshire
GB3ML	Blackhill, Central Scotland
GB3MW	Leamington Spa
GB3NS	Banstead, Surrey
GB3NU	Benbecula, Western Isles
GB3PB	Peterborough, Cambridgeshire
GB3PD	Peterhead, Grampian
GB3WY	Queensbury, W. Yorks

RB11: 434.875MHz Input, 433.275MHz Output

GB3AH	Nr. Swaffam, Norfolk
GB3BK	10km West of Reading, Berks
GB3DC	Sunderland
GB3GR	Near Grantham, Lincs
GB3GY	Grimsby, South Humberside
GB3HN	Hitchin, Herts
GB3HT	Hinkley, Leicestershire
GB3LA	Leeds

GB3LR   Lewes, East Sussex
GB3NF   7km South of Southampton
GB3RE   Chatham, Kent
GB3SH   5km East of Honiton, Devon
GB3WP   Hyde, Near Manchester
GB3ZI   Stafford, Staffs.

RB12: 434.900MHz Input, 433.300MHz Output

GB3GM   Paisley, Renfrewshire
GB3MT   Bolton, Lancs
GB3PT   Barkway, Hertfordshire
GB3RY   Leicester

RB13: 434.925MHz Input, 433.325HMz Output

GB3CA   Carlisle, Cumbria
GB3CY   York
GB3DS   Worksop, Nottinghamshire
GB3GF   Guildford, Surrey
GB3GU   Guernsey
GB3HW   Gidea Park, Essex
GB3LC   Louth, Lincolnshire
GB3SM   Near Leek, Staffordshire
GB3TD   Swindon, Wiltshire
GB3VH   Hatfield, Hertfordshire
GB3XX   Daventry

RB14: 434.950MHz Input, 433.350MHz Output

GB3AB   Aberdeen
GB3CB   Birmingham, West Midlands
GB3CE   Wivenhoe, Colchester, Essex
GB3ED   Edinburgh
GB3GL   Glasgow
GB3HE   Hastings, Sussex
GB3HK   Hawick, Borders
GB3HR   Stanmore, Middlesex
GB3LF   Lancaster
GB3MR   Park Moor, Stockport, Cheshire
GB3ND   Barnstaple, Devon
GB3PY   Cambridge
GB3SD   Weymouth, Dorset
GB3TS   Middlesborough, Cleveland
GB3WF   Otley, Near Leeds
GB3YL   Lowestoft, Suffolk

RB15: 434.975MHz Input, 433.375MHz Output

GB3BF	Carlton, North Bedfordshire
GB3FN	Farnham, Surrey
GB3HB	St. Austell, Cornwall
GB3LH	Lyth Hill, Near Shrewsbury
GB3OM	Omagh, Northern Ireland
GB3OX	Oxford, Oxfordshire
GB3PP	Preston, Lancashire
GB3SG	Cardiff
GB3SU	Sudbury, Suffolk
GB3SZ	Bournemouth, Dorset
GB3TH	Tamworth, Staffs
GB3WI	Wisbech, Cambridgeshire
GB3WU	Wakefield, Yorkshire

APPENDIX 3 – USEFUL CONTACTS

Equipment Suppliers

A.J.H. Electronics, 151a Bilton Road, Rugby. CV22 7AS
Tel. 0788 76473
(Varying stocks of ex-PMR equipment).

Anchor Surplus Ltd, Cattle Market, Nottingham. NG2 3GY
Tel. 0602 864902
(Large and constantly changing stocks of ex-government
equipment).

B. Bamber Electronics, 5 Station Road, Littleport, Cambs.
Tel. 0353 860185
(Regular sales and auctions of ex-PMR equipment).

Garex Electronics, Harrow House, Akeman Street, Tring. HP23 6AA
Tel. 044 282 8580
(Stocks of ex-PMR equipment and PCB modules, together with
suitable mobile whip aerials).

Raycom Communication Systems Ltd., International House,
963 Wolverhampton Rd, Oldbury, Warley. West Midlands.
(Varying stocks of ex-PMR equipment and modification kits).

Crystal Suppliers

Golledge Electronics, Merriott, Somerset. TA16 5NS
Tel. 0460 73718
(Suppliers of crystals and replacement crystal filters).

McKnight Crystals, Hardley Industrial Estate, Hythe,
Southampton SO4 6ZY
Tel. 0703 848961
(Suppliers of made-to-order crystals to amateur specifications)

PM Electronic Services, 2 Alexander Drive, Heswall, Wirral,
Merseyside, L61 6XT
Tel. 051 342 4443
(Suppliers of ex-stock crystals on popular channels and made-to-
order crystals).

QuartsLab Marketing Ltd., P.O. Box 19, Erith. Kent. DA8 1LH
Tel. 01 318 4419/0322 330830
(Suppliers of ex-stock crystals on popular channels and made-to-
order crystals, regular rally attendances).

Component Suppliers

These suppliers hold stocks of components required for the modification of sets, all publish comprehensive catalogues at a nominal cost as well as providing a mail order service.

Cirkit Distribution Ltd. Park Lane, Broxbourne, Herts. E10 7NQ
Tel. 0992 441306
(Suppliers of preamp kits and ceramic resonators as well as general components)

Maplin Electronics PLC. P.O. Box 3, Rayleigh, Essex. SS6 8LR
Tel. 0702 554155
(Large stock of general components at low cost)

General Amateur Radio Information

Radio Society of Great Britain, Lambda House, Cranborne Road, Potters Bar, Herts. EN6 3JE
Tel. 0707 59015

INDEX

Subscribe now...
here's 3 good reasons why!

CITIZEN'S BAND is the only British CB magazine and covers a wide ra[nge] topics of interest to the newcomer and the experienced user. In each [issue] the latest equipment is reviewed, useful practical projects are detailed all the national and international band news is featured. Of particular interest to overseas readers are the QSL pages, articles on shortwav[e] listening, and reports on VHF CB.

ETI is Britain's leading magazine for the electr[onic] enthusiast and is renow[ned] for its ability to keep pa[ce] with the leading edge [of] technology, offering bo[th] practical and theoretica[l] examples in the form [of] D.I.Y. projects and deta[iled] technical explanations. single-source guide to tomorrow's microchip world.

[H]AM RADIO TODAY caters for both the [ex]perienced user and newcomer to [a]mateur radio. With generally [in]formative features, the latest news and [p]ractical projects, this magazine covers all aspects of this growing field; [a]n invaluable compliment for any licenced radio amateur worldwide.

[If] you would like to subscribe to any of these magazines, please make [yo]ur cheque or money order payable to A.S.P. LTD or send your [Ac]cess/Barclaycard number to the following address.

	UK	EUROPE	MIDDLE EAST	FAR EAST	REST OF THE WORLD
[ET]I	£18.00	£22.20	£22.40	£24.00	£22.70
[H]AM RADIO TODAY	£16.80	£21.30	£21.50	£23.20	£21.80

Send your remittance to:
The Subscription Manager (CG23)
Argus Specialist Publications, Argus House